THE UNTOUCHABLE PLAYERS

BY

VINCENT A. STEELE

TABLE OF CONTENTS

COPYRIGHTS

DEDICATION

TO THE KINGS OF FUNK THE "OHIO PLAYERS"

ACKNOWLEDGMENT

First off, thank You for being here! I am very very grateful to the multi-platinum recording artist Marshall "Rock" Jones my brother from another, and Greg Webster of the Grammy Award-winning "Ohio Players." Thank you for giving me amazing interviews to work with. I am grateful to my brother Tommy Black for the introduction to Marshall, my team that has worked on the movie with me for years Lisa Cummings, Robert Martin, Kashu Xola, Tommie Clemons. Jabari Ali for always holding me down, Leah Daniels for helping change the script direction, Bill Duke for being the first director to write notes to the movies script, and Chase Parker, thank you for helping this book take its form.

Last but definitely not least, Special thanks to my wife and family for giving me every opportunity to be as creative as I can be.

INTRODUCTION

Welcome to my world!!! It's the year 1979 and
bright early on a Tuesday morning. Here we have
thirty-eight-year-old Marshall "Rock" Jones dressed
sharply in his brown leather jacket and a sleek white
turban, Marshall walking up to the door, mumbling
"This Backstabbing bastard," looking mad as a
motherfucker! Marshall yells "Yo!" while banging
on the front door of this nice upscale home in
Dayton, Ohio. He begins to get extremely frustrated
as no one has come to the door. He started tapping
his foot, then proceeds to bang the door with even
more authority, commanding a response! Suddenly,
a matted-looking afro, along with the face of
someone that looked like he's been to the moon and
back three times, opens the door. Marshall looks
pissed off and is not going for the pathetic look that
the thirty-eight-year-old Clarence "Satch" Satchell
is trying to give him, Satch standing in the doorway
looking as he was woken from what looked to be a
coffin. He then tries to say something but is bumped
out of the way by Marshall as he barges his way
into the house. Satch's demeanor changes fast, this
doesn't sit well with him, and he closes the door
shaking his head.

NOW HOLD ON! Before I even go there, let me tell you how it all began!!! Ok, follow me, it's the year 1958, to the Westside of Dayton, Ohio. Here we have seventeen-year-old Marshall dressed poorly, walking into his mother's front door with a smile on his face and a mean bop to his step. As Marshall enters the living room, he sees his older sister sitting on the couch rolling her eyes at him as soon as she sees him, then she sucks her teeth at Marshall. Then, she puts her lip up and turns her back to Marshall like he ain't shit. Marshall's older brother, Ted, begins to walk down the stairs; seeing Marshall, he starts to shake his head in disgust. Ted had a wicked grin on his face, making Marshall's lively bop start to diminish as he walks into the kitchen. Marshall's mother is a thirty-eight-year-old dark-skinned stern-looking black woman whose back is turned as she chops pieces of meat loudly on a wooden chopping board next to her bible. Marshall walks in the room, and without his mother turning around or hearing Marshall say a word, she says, "Marshall, I know it's you!" Playing cool, Marshall tries to be sarcastic to make her smile. "Okay, Ma, what I do now?" Marshal's mother turns around, looking irate, pointing her knife at him, yelling, "BOY, LET ME TELL YOU SOMETHING, AIN'T NO BROKE MOTHERFUCKER LIVING UNDER MY ROOF... YOU GOTTA GO!" Marshall, being remorseful, tried to walk over to his mother with his arms open, but she pointed the knife at him, saying, "Look, I didn't lose your job... I know where mine is! You fucked up, had a baby, then lost your job?"

Marshall, ashamed and embarrassed, put his head down. Then, Marshall's mother looks him up and down again, and with disgust in her voice, she says, "Trying to be some kind of musician. NIGGA YOU AIN'T GONNA BE SHIT! JUST LIKE YOUR PAPPY!" Marshall picks his head up to say something but sees the look on his mother's face that said about ten thousand bad words. Marshall puts his head back down, and his mother lets him have it. "WHAT? DON'T LOOK AT ME FOR NO SYMPATHY! GET THE FUCK OUT OF MY HOUSE!" Marshall, defeated, tries to walk back towards the front door, but his mother, continually pointing the knife at him, yells, "WHERE YOU GOING! Your shit on the back porch! Just like your pappy shit was!" Marshall starts to walk past his mother towards the back porch, looking deflated. He tries to stop, but she looks him up and down, disgusted. Then she points at the back door with the knife in her hand and an angry look on her face.

December 28th, 1958 on a cold winter night, walking off the stage at his old job at Dayton Band, is a seventeen-year-old Marshall looking defeated.

An older white woman on stage holding a clipboard shaking her head while looking down at Marshall as he exits the stage yells, "PEOPLE, IF YOU CANNOT PLAY MUSIC, JUST LEAVE! DON'T WASTE MY TIME AND YOURS!" Marshall, walking away from the stage, is approached by a short, well-dressed black trumpeter/trombonist, twenty-two-year-old Ralph "Pee Wee " Middlebrooks. Pee Wee is very loud, very outspoken, and just loves to make fun of everyone. Pee Wee, trying to get Marshall's attention, says, "Hey man!" Marshall, ashamed and nervous, keeps walking and Pee Wee follows him, saying, "That white lady doesn't know shit! Man, I caught you playing with that little band last week; you good!" Pee Wee stops walking behind Marshall, who doesn't respond. Pee Wee loudly says, "I know it's ain't none of my business, but how much bread are you lookin' to get with these cats?"

Marshall's curiosity arouses; he stops and turns around, saying, "Why, you looking to join Dayton Band too?" Pee Wee shakes his head, gesturing no you don't get it, then he answers proudly, "Nah! I gotta a band! The Ohio Untouchables! Look, we got a gig tonight, and we need a bass player." Marshall starts grinning, ready to say yes, but Pee Wee stops him saying, "Now, hold on! You gotta hold that bottom tho, ya dig?" Marshall extends his hand, introducing himself Marshall, Marshall Jones. Pee Wee responds, "Ralph Meadowbrooks, but Pee Wee will do." Marshall steps back, admiring Pee Wee's clothing, thinking he has big money. Marshall quickly snaps out of groupie mode and replies, "I got a baby; we talking about some real money, right?"

Pee Wee looks Marshall up and down. "I look broke or something?" Marshall looks at Pee Wee's clothes then says, "OK, does it come with a wardrobe?" Pee Wee proudly replies, "Come over to my pad, a wardrobe? Baby I got clothes!" At Pee Wee's house, he laid out some pants, shirts, and jackets on the bed for Marshall to choose from. Marshall grabs an outfit and goes to the bathroom, but fights to get in the tight pants. Pee Wee, standing there looking confused, staring at the bathroom door hearing Marshall knocking stuff over in there. Marshall yells through the door, "Man, I really appreciate you letting me crash for a while, but damn! These pants are too tight, too short; I don't know about these, Pee Wee!"

Marshall comes out looking ridiculous in Pee Wee's pants. Marshall dressed in some real short black pants (high-waters) and a shirt that's too small too. Then Marshall goes over to the mirror, and through the mirror, he sees Pee Wee shaking his head and holding his mouth to stop from laughing out loud, and Marshall says, "Man, they look like my little brother's pants! I can't go on stage like this!" Pee Wee puts his hand on Marshall's shoulder, looking at Marshall in the eyes through the mirror, then starts to chuckle while saying, "Yes, you can, Jack! Cause this gig gon get you some money, to buy you some new pants! And fast!" Marshall sees Pee Wee smiling while holding himself back from laughing. Marshall shakes his head in the mirror as he looks at himself; he then says, "Man, whatever! I can dig it, and thanks Pee Wee."

Later that night, the band is on stage playing to a packed house in Club 51. Marshall is on bass, Pee Wee on trumpet, and three other band members are on stage, closing their set. At the lead is "Robert Ward," playing his guitar, looks over to Pee Wee, then puts his thumb up as his approval of adding Marshall to the band. Marshall seeing this, smiles to himself. Two songs later, the band closes their set to a cheering crowd. The announcer walks on stage and says, "Let's give it up to Dayton's hottest band "The Ohio Untouchables!" We got more for y'all, stick around." Leaving the stage, the bass player Marshall's filling in for approaches Robert looking really dusty. Pee Wee points to show Marshall. The bass player approaches Robert saying, "Robert... let me talk to you for a minute?"

Robert keeps walking while entertaining the female groupies walking beside him as he exits the stage. The bass player calls out to Robert's name loud enough that Robert stops, then he smiles at the ladies and begins to give one of the meanest struts towards the bass player. Robert, with a smile on his face, walks straight up to the bass player, being charismatic, and he says, "Look who shows up now. What the fuck you want, man?" The bass player, knowing that Robert's nothing to play with, takes his hat off, smiling at him, and he says, "I'm good now! I want back in the band." Robert smiles at the ladies then turns around, pissed off, and gets even closer in his face. "Listen motherfucker; I don't want you back! Trying to fuck my shit up, this be my band, my legacy, and nobody gonna fuck this up! Robert looks him up and down, and the bass player puts his head down, then Robert says, "Besides, I like that black little motherfucker!"

Marshall walks over to his friend that drove him and Pee Wee there, looking amazed as Pee Wee has hinted he was in the band. Marshall stretches his arm out and starts to point towards Robert. "You see, Robert Ward, he's the leader of the group and from what I heard the Ike Turner type. Robert is better than everybody in the band. The only problem with that is he knows it too. Besides singing, Robert plays the guitar with a really unique vibrato tone coming from his Magnatone Amplifier. And in Dayton, he is the hottest thing out!" Marshall then stops smiling as he points at Cornelius "Cornbread" Johnson, talking to some ladies saying, "Along with Robert, is 21 years old Cornelius "Cornbread" Johnson, from Luthersville, Georgia. From what I heard, a real cool cat, solid drummer, and the ladies' man of the group."

Marshall points over to Clarence "Satch" Satchell, they see him with a lady playing in his hair, and Marshall says, "And on saxophone is 17-year-old Clarence "Satch" Satchell; this guy looks and acts like a pimp. Up on-stage, we had something special tonight, so to be a part of this band means everything to me!" Pee Wee walks up, then he winks at Robert, then taps Marshall on the shoulder and gestures come here. "Robert said you in! Here, take your money! Now go buy you something dat fits!" Marshall takes the money, then he grabs Pee Wee by the arm as he tries to walk away. Marshall looks Pee Wee in his eyes, then says, "The money is good! But I really think we can make it big! So I'm in!"

Marshall shakes Pee Wee's hand, then he stands back with a pleased look on his face, looking at everyone from the group interacting with each other, then he walks back over to his friend slapping him in the back with his pay, and then there is Marshall getting congratulated by his friend.

A few months later, in 5th Street Night Club, Marshall sitting down after a set, sees a fine light-skinned girl named Janet standing on the other side of the room staring at him. Janet, with her two sexy friends, is starring and waving to get Marshall's attention. After getting his attention, Janet seductively walks over to him. Janet starts flirting while touching Marshall. "Hey, baby, how you doing? I heard y'all playin', you sound real good." Marshall starts checking her out, standing with his tongue out, looking very interested. Janet turns around real slow to show off her skimpy dress and her amazing figure. Janet stops turning, seeing Marshall's still looking at her ass. "You like what you see sexy?" Marshall licks his lips, enjoying the view, then replies, "Shit, and anybody in their right mind." Janet grabs Marshall's hand and puts it up her dress. Then she looks Marshall straight in his eyes as he has his hand up her skirt in amazement, and says, "Say, baby, maybe we can work something out. I see you like it, imagine how many of your friends will too." Marshall's eyes pop open, looking at her, shocked. "Wait! You want me to be your pimp?" Janet puts her bright red lips close to his ear, whispering, "You way too much man for one woman, you see my two friends over there?"

Marshall looks to the other side of the room to see the two girls smiling and waving at him. Marshall smiles back at them, then says, "OK, when can you start?" The next week Marshall is sitting in the car with his older brother Ted (25, Black, tough exterior, doesn't trust anyone.) Ted turns to Marshall with the big brother I don't believe shit look and says, "Marshall, why you got me out here, wit that big old stupid smile on your face?" "Ted, I'm pimpin! I done got me some hoes." Ted, rolling a joint, laughs at Marshall. "What you smoking? You got no game!" Marshall, with everything to prove, confidently replies, "Don't believe me, fine! I'll show you better than I can tell you." They see Janet coming out of one car and going into the next one in the parking lot. Marshall points to her to show Ted. "There she is, you see the girl in the red shorts." Ted replies, "Her, she just went from one car to the next? I saw her thirty minutes ago. Man, when you getting paid?" Marshall pauses briefly, then answers, "Yeah, I should go check on my money."

Fifteen minutes pass before Janet gets out of the car she was in, and Marshall gets out of the car, and she looks directly at Marshall before getting into another car. Then Ted says, "She ain't say nothing to you?" Ted starts to laugh, and Marshall puts his head down and gets back in the car. Twenty minutes go by, and Janet is still in a black car parked off to the side of the parking lot. Ted messing with Marshall, wakes him from a daze, tapping him, saying, "Jones... Jones?" Marshall, back from his daze, gets out of the car looking really nervous and goes over to the car that Janet's in. Getting closer, Marshall sees the front driver's window is rolled down. In the driver's seat is a pimp Marshall knew from around town. Marshall is now standing over Valerie in the back seat, who is not looking at him at all.

Marshall musters up the courage to say something "So you ain't going to say nothing? All of a sudden, a big cloud of marijuana smoke hits Marshall dead in his face, and Marshall turns to the driver's window to see it's a local pimp that he knew from the club, and he says, "Look here, man! You don't belong here, young blood, stick to your music! This is my world!!!" Marshall glances over to Janet, who's looking pathetic. Marshall starts to walk off, but stops hearing Janet's pimp saying, "Don't be mad at her, she's just doing her job. Pimps are made, but players are born!" Marshall walks away looking defeated, then into his brother's car to a laughing Ted. Let's just say Ted was right Marshall had no game!

By this time, the hang out was at Satch's father's Barbershop, Where the band got their conk hairstyles, and the ladies passed by to admire the hottest band in Dayton, Ohio. The next weekend, the band is waiting in the dressing room of the Patio Lounge Night Club before going on stage for another show. Then Robert shows up late with his manservant, Harry (25-years-old, 6 foot 2 inches, and medium build.) Robert walks in, talking real fast. "Ok, everybody's here?" Nobody says anything, and Pee Wee glances over at Sugarfoot, who is sitting off to the side playing chess with Marshall. Pee Wee walking out of the room, heading for the stage, being sarcastic, says, "Yeah, everyone's here now our fearless leader." Robert chuckles in a devilish manner, then says, "Then what fuck y'all, sitting round here for? Marshall, being irritated, looks at Sugarfoot and says, "Here we go." Cutting him off is another knock at the door, and it's the stagehand.

With the door open, you could hear the announcer calling the "Ohio Untouchables" to the stage as they hurry to go on stage. Robert stands in the doorway with his grinning manservant Harry. The last to leave from the back of the room is Marshall, followed by Sugarfoot, who is there to perform with another band. Robert taps Harry as Sugarfoot walks by and says, "Who's this big head motherfucker?" Sugarfoot stops and turns around unafraid, answering Robert with his thick country accent.

"What? Because the MC is calling the band to come, Robert stalls then turns to meet the band on the stage.

Robert walks up on stage as if the band was playing for his entrance; the audience can be heard cheering. Robert hits the stage, ready to go at the lead, grabbing the mic. "How y'all doing? Hope you cats are ready to get down!?" Robert attracts every ounce of attention he could find, playing up to his huge ego. "Yeah, baby, get ready for the baddest!" Aggravated, playing on-stage, Marshall turns to Satch. "Look at this motherfucker. Cornbread starts to get equally frustrated "Man, sing the damn song, stupid. Satch says "What the fuck is he waiting for?" Pee Wee answers, "His fan club."

Cornbread plays a drop on the one, thinking that might get Robert to start singing the song. Robert turns around away from the mic to give Cornbread a look that cuts real deep and says, "I'll tell you when to start the damn song!" Cornbread does not look up at Robert; he just keeps playing. Marshall looks at Pee Wee and says in a low tone. "Here we go with this shit again. Robert's ostentatious behavior intended to impress the audience hits its pentacle, and Robert says, "Y'all ready!!!!" Robert begins to play the song for the cheering crowd while the band is still playing something jazzy. Pee Wee and Satch shake their heads, having no desire to blow their vibe, trying to compete with Robert's ego. Off to the side, you see Thelma Gordy with her cousin looking at the door to see if Berry is coming. Pee Wee turns to Satch between horn lines. "keep it steady, you dig?" "...Yeah, whatever." Robert signaled for something new again, but due to him not showing up to practice, the band has no idea what he's talking about, and Robert starts to unravel. At the side of the stage, during their set, Robert walks over to a 6' 4" 260lb Soundman, looking angry and speaking loudly. "Aye! I told you, I need more Robert in the front monitor." The Soundman looks at Robert like he's crazy being as big as he is. "I already turned you up louder than I wanted to! It's not happening!" Robert stands his ground. "I can't hear myself! Just do your job! This is my shit!" Seeing Robert getting pissed, the Soundman starts to fuck with him and says, "Everyone else hears you, superstar! It's ain't happening!" Robert, pissed off, returns to his place on stage, but after a few opening bars of the song, Robert walks off the stage, and the band stops playing and reluctantly starts following him. The last one to leave the stage to a booing crowd is Marshall shaking his head.

The next week, the band is in Club 5100, relaxing after a set. Robert is bragging to two ladies over by the bar while the rest of the band is sitting around a pool table away from the bar. Pee Wee and Harry are playing pool. Pee Wee walks over to the table where Marshall is sitting, smiling, then he winks his eye at Marshall, then takes a sip from his drink, and walks back to the pool table. Pee Wee knocks down the eight ball on the table, not saying a word. Harry, mad as hell, walks over and slaps ten bucks in Pee Wee's hand. Then, Pee Wee puts chalk on his pool stick and says, "You're 6 foot 2 inches of pure stupid!" Pointing to Robert's Lackey Harry, Marshall replies, "how much did you get this sucker for tonight?" Pee Wee smiles, puts the chalk down, and goes over to the pool table. The bait worked as Harry, hearing all this walks back over to the pool table and starts to rack the balls, saying, "Let me try to win my money back, big mouth!"

Robert walks up, smiling, and says, "Hey ya'll, she said we need bigger shows. That's right, Robert needs more money!" Marshall turns to Robert and says, "Bigger shows! What bout the ones we got? The ones you keep missing?" Robert being nonchalant, says, "What? I ain't got time for this bullshit!" Robert waves his hand at Marshall, then walks back over to the bar. Harry goes to break and barely hits the balls, and Pee Wee laughs loud.

Then Pee Wee winks at Marshall and takes his turn, missing on purpose. Marshall shakes his head and walks off. "Your turn, and you better not miss that easy shot!" Harry, with an easy shot, misses and scratches the ball. Pee Wee lets him have it "Wash your ass, cause you keep scratching, you blind motherfucker!" Pee Wee grabs his shot glass and gulps down his shot, then slams it on the table, saying, "Combo, 3 to the 5 in the corner pocket. The combo goes in, and Harry begins to steam; he looks to see what Robert is doing. Harry sees Robert sitting and talking to a woman on the sofa, not looking at him. Then Harry grabs the smaller Pee Wee by the shirt, roughing up Pee Wee. Marshall returns from the restroom to see Harry tussling with Pee Wee then, all he hears is Marshall running and yelling. "PICK ON SOMEBODY YOUR OWN SIZE!"

Harry being bigger is getting the best of Pee Wee. Marshall tackles Harry but that was about all he could do with Harry being so much bigger than him too. Harry starts to beat Marshall, Pee Wee jumps on Harry's back. Robert rushes over to grab Marshall, who is now punching Harry, and shouts, "stay the fuck out of this man!" Marshall, still looking to jump in, is not looking at Robert as he grabs him. "What you mean, stay out of it! Fuck you, Harry! Wait till Robert lets me go!" Robert grabs Marshall by the neck, pushing him to the wall, and then picks him up by his neck. Harry and Pee Wee seeing this, stopped tussling to watch.

Robert holding Marshall in the air by the neck says, "You little motherfucker, I'll walk your ass to hell!" Marshall doesn't move. Robert lets go of him and walks away with Harry. The two go sit down with the lady that Robert was talking to. Marshall then runs behind the bar and begins throwing bottle after bottle at Robert, trying to hit him. "TAKE THAT, AND THAT, YOU UNGRATEFUL BASTARD!" Robert ducks, almost getting hit, and yells, "I'm going to kill you!" Before Robert could get to Marshall, the owners and security break it up and save Marshall from getting his butt whooped. Robert walks out pissed off at Marshall, and Harry follows close behind Robert. Later you see Marshall, with one foot on the wall and his head down, is approached by Pee Wee, looking concerned with a bottle of wine in his hand. "Look, before you start, I don't want no parts of this band! Fuck Robert and this band!" Marshall keeps his head down, and Pee Wee gets in his face. Pee Wee bends down to look Marshall in his face, then says, "Fuck me too! Come on, Marshall, don't do it for that motherfucker." Marshall keeps his head down. "I don't need this bullshit! Money ain't the reason I'm here. I really thought we had something special." Pee Wee replies, "Is it worth fighting for?" Marshall picks his head up. "Pee Wee, I trust you; you brought me in but, Robert is –" Pee Wee puts his hand up, gesturing to Marshall to stop. "Robert's an ass! And every family has one." Marshall, hearing the word family, smirks, then Pee Wee hands Marshall the bottle of wine. Marshall smiles at Pee Wee shaking his head, then grabs a drink. "Every time Robert leaves the goddamn stage, I lose it!" Marshall grabs Pee Wee by the shoulders and looks him in the eyes, smiling, then says," Keep playing! We ain't gonna stop!" Pee Wee, confused, pauses, then nods his head of approval. "You right!" Pee Wee gives Marshall a high five. Pee Wee looks at Marshall smiling. "C'mon, let's go! Plus, you need this bread, so you can get your ass off my couch." The two walk off, then Pee Wee trips Marshall, but Marshall catches himself.

Robert West, the owner of Lupine Records, is thirty-nine years old, Afro-American, and a straight shooter. Robert West is talking to the band in his Detroit office in the year 1962. Robert turns to the band and says, "I heard a lot about you boys. So, I had some of my people check y'all out." Robert West, smiling, looks to Wilson Pickett. "Well, you can thank Wilson Pickett because we're gonna pick you boys up." The band members all jump with excitement. Robert West puts his hands out. "Now, hold on! Wait a minute; It'll be to back the Falcons. Now, you boys prove your worth! Then we can see about signing you and extending your stay with us."

Robert shakes Robert West's hand, saying, "That's fine, mighty fine, but after a little taste of Robert Ward, you gon want a whole lot!" Robert West smirks and says, "All right now, I expect to hear a good recording." The band looks at Robert disgusted, then displays their joy with gratitude and handshakes with Robert West.

Outside the studio, Marshall and Pee Wee, going round back to smoke a joint, see a fourteen-year-old boy playing a stand-up right bass sounding terrible. Pee Wee seeing the look on Marshall's eyes, starts gesturing for Marshall to leave it alone, but it doesn't work, and Marshall heads for the young man and says, "Let me see that." The young man gives it to Marshall, and he plays it so well the young man gets excited, then Marshall hands it to him and says, "I put in a lot of work. Working at Dayton Band, I learned how to assemble instruments every day, so I took a liking to the bass. My friend had an old yellow guitar with no strings; I gave him three bucks for it! Then, I took it to Dayton Band and drilled holes in the headstock of the guitar, making it my tuning key. This is how creative you have to be to create your sound. Miss this upright though, I played my first song on one of these." Pee Wee, hearing this song and dance, already pulls Marshall's arm then points to his watch, and Marshall says, "Nothing stops a dream but the dreamer." They both continue to walk to the back of the building.

The year 1962 and Thelma Gordy in her late 20s and fine walks into the recording studio's control room. The producer, a thirty-year-old white American male with a small frame, jumps out of his chair to greet Thelma Gordy at the door. Thelma taking her coat off, catches the attention of the men in the studio, and she says, "Sorry for being late; this separation has me all over the place." The producer, smiling, says, "No problem, Mrs. Gordy, this seats for you." The producer leans over the massive control board to talk through his state-of-the-art Crosstalk, and he says, "OK, is everyone in place?" The band in the recording booth pauses, and Robert sarcastically answers through the Crosstalk, "Ready!" Marshall leans over to Satch and, in a low tone and Marshall says, "Yeah! This time." Satch, smirking, replies in a low tone as the mics were on, "Let's see the motherfucker walk off now!" The producer talks to the band through the crosstalk, "OK, let's get a level. Everyone, please test your mics."

Everyone starts checking their microphones by doing vocal harmonies to the delight of the producer and Thelma. The producer, being amazed, jumps up and presses the button to the Crosstalk, and he says, "That's good, now let's hear some music. Ready on

3! 1, 2 3." The band begins to play the instrumental
to "Your Love Is Real" by the Ohio Untouchables
on the producer's cue. The band plays, then the
producer says, "OK, that's good, thanks." The band
stops playing, and the producer presses the
Crosstalk and says, "Are you ready, Robert?" He
sees Robert looking serious as he replies, "Ready!"
The producer's eyes opened wide, seeing how
confidently Robert replied to him. Marshall, leaning
over to Pee Wee and says, "Here we go." The band,
alongside Wilson Pickett, began recording Wilson
Pickett's first hit record, "I Found A Love." Later
that day, the band returned to the studio to see a
sign on studio 1's door reading, "The B-side to 'I
Found a Love' is called 'The Swim.'" Marshall and
the band look into the room to see the studio
engineers filling a bathtub full of water, and Satch
says, "Their recording techniques are creative."
Then, Satch lights a cigarette walking off towards a
female intern with a mean strut.

The next week band is on stage playing "Your Love
Is Real" by The Ohio Untouchables. The band starts
the song, and Robert starts singing to some girls in
the front row while playing his guitar. Marshall
looks over his shoulder to see a skinny bucktooth
girl smiling at him. Marshall turns away quickly,
but he sees Satch and Pee Wee staring at him,
nodding their head for approval. Marshall laughs

while shaking his head in disapproval. Robert signals something new to Cornbread, but Cornbread doesn't get it. Robert tries again, then gets frustrated and walks off the stage. Cornbread stops along with Satch, but Marshall and Pee Wee kept playing. Then Satch and Cornbread reluctantly join in. They see Robert stop dead in his track walking in the crowd, hearing the music playing. Robert looks at them, then returns to the stage, trying to play it off. Pee Wee looks over to Marshall, nodding his head yes.

Fall, the year is 1963, and the band is in Lupine's Recording studio for a photoshoot. Playing in the background, their song, "Forgive Me Darling," could be heard by the "Ohio Untouchables." Thelma Gordy and Robert West are standing next to the cameraman, who is looking into his camera. The band, Robert, Marshall, Cornbread, Pee Wee, and Satch, are standing with their instruments, ready for the picture. Marshall looks over at Robert, pissed, and Pee Wee nudges him to stop. The cameraman looking through the lens says, "Mrs. Gordy, I think you're gonna love this picture. READY SMILE!" Thelma looks at Cornbread in a seductive manner while replying to the cameraman, "I'm really lovin' somethin' 'bout this band." With no one looking, Thelma blows a kiss at Cornbread as soon as he locks eyes with her. The cameraman, seeing this acts like he didn't. Robert smiles, and the cameraman takes the picture for Robert Ward's Hot Stuff Album cover.

The band shows up to a packed house in Detroit; the marquee shows "Love Is Amazing" by Robert Ward and the Untouchables. Marshall gets out of the Limo and points to the marquee to show Pee Wee mad as hell then, he says, "You believe this jackass! Robert and the Untouchables? Like we ain't doin' the fuckin work!" They see Marshall pissed off, looking at Robert, talking to some ladies under the marquee. Marshall walks towards Robert, mad to say something, but Pee Wee jumps in front of him, stopping him. "I know! But look at these motherfucker's faces; they excited, no need to burst their bubble. we'll talk 'bout this tomorrow!" Marshall, mad as hell, says, "Don't get me wrong, I am happy to see us in lights but damn!" Satch comes out of the Limo yelling, "HEADLINING... YEAH, BABY, THIS IS FOR REAL, MAN!!!" You see Marshall looking at the marquee that says Robert Ward and The Ohio Untouchables. The Ohio Untouchables become a force to be reckoned with in 1964 man, do things really start rolling at this point. The band is back and forth between labels Lu Pine Productions and Thelma Record Co. 1964 the band records their second record with Lu Pine records ``Nobody does Something for Nothing."

Followed by "Your Love Is Real," recorded by Thelma Record Co., returning to the airwaves as Robert Ward and The Untouchables.

CHAPTER ONE

DRESSING ROOM OF THE 20 GRAND - NIGHT - FALL 1964

There's sweet blues music playing in the background. Sugarfoot and the band without Robert are backstage, looking angry. Pee Wee, being outspoken, sets the tone in the quiet room "Fuckin' Robert ain't here to hit the stage again, that's what I know!" Marshall throws his bag on the couch, pissed and turned to everyone in a stern tone. "We ain't fuckin this tour up, Thirty-One-Nighters? Man, fuck that. Sugar, you in?" Sugarfoot, with his head down, smirks. Cornbread smirks while saying, "Marshall, good thing you called Sugarfoot."

Sugarfoot smiles and, through the door, enters the stagehand. "They calling you guys to come on stage. Marshall walks to the door with Pee Wee smiling and saying, "C'mon, you lazy motherfuckers!" The band hits the stage with Sugarfoot as their new frontman. The band starts performing "I'm Tired" by The Ohio Untouchables with Sugarfoot at the lead, singing with his guitar. Pee Wee and Satch are mesmerizing the dancing crowd with their horns. Then Sugarfoot turns around, looking nervous and facing Marshall with his head down, playing his guitar. Satch, concerned, looks at Marshall and says, "Why does he always do that?" Marshall, still playing, leans over to Satch and says, "He said he gets distracted by the crowd! But he's just nervous." Satch winks at Marshall and starts to dance around Sugarfoot while playing his sax. Then Satch hooks Sugarfoot's arm to his arm and turns Sugarfoot around to face the audience, and the two of them start to rock the crowd. A group of groupies makes their way to the front, and Sugarfoot lets loose a mean guitar solo while Satch steps back and the girls go wild. The band leaves the stage to the crowd going crazy.

A groupie (female fan) grabs Sugarfoot and puts her panties with her number written on them in Sugarfoot's pocket. "You were amazing." Sugarfoot, not sure what the groupie put in his pocket, looks down to see what it is, and the groupie kisses him on his cheek. Sugarfoot looks up smiling and says, "Thanks, Suga!" the groupie flirting, replies, "Now you better use it!" The groupie goes to her friends, waiting to congratulate her. While the band was on stage playing their second set, Robert shows up late for the gig, making a big fuss as he makes his way to the stage. Marshall sees this and leans over to Pee Wee and says, "Robert's here." Robert starts arguing with the nightclub staff, pointing at the stage. Pee Wee is mouthing the word "Fuck." Pee Wee goes over to warn Sugarfoot, singing to the groupie that just gave him her panties in the front row. Pee Wee taps Sugarfoot and points to Robert, saying, "Man, I hate to do this to you, but Robert just showed up." Sugarfoot's demeanor changes as he looks at Pee Wee like he could kill him, "It's cool, man! But you motherfuckers better not call me ever again!"

The band stops playing as Robert makes his way on the stage and approaches Sugarfoot, who is already packing his things. "Get the fuck off my stage! This be Robert Ward's night!" Sugarfoot waves his hand, gesturing whatever. Then he turns to Robert and says, "Whatever, man. The early bird gets the worm, but the second mouse gets the cheese." Robert steps to the smaller Sugarfoot, trying to punk him.

"You heard what I said!" Sugarfoot, unafraid, puts his guitar down and faces Robert with a straight face and stern voice, and says, "Listen, get your punk ass on stage, and everything will be alright! Touch me, and you won't be able to wipe your ass when I get through with you, motherfucker. Robert looks to see if anybody heard what Sugarfoot just told him; seeing no one heard, he walks on stage. Then, he looks back to make sure Sugarfoot is gone.

DAYTON, OHIO - AFTERNOON - DECEMBER 1964

The song "Your Love Is Real" plays by the Ohio Untouchables. A mid-western accent can be heard, with a deep smoker's voice. The RADIO DJ says, "The phone line ain't stopped ringing about this new Ohio Untouchable record! Let's give it up for "Your Love Is Real!" This band is also known for putting on a heck of a show round town, and at this point, I don't see anything stopping this group from becoming Dayton's own superstars." Robert hearing this smirks while in his brand new Black Cadillac, driving slowly through the snow in Downtown Dayton, Ohio. Vintage cars can be seen from the sixties, snowed in downtown. Vintage record shops are also on the block, vintage concert halls, and plenty of white businessmen walking the streets in vintage coats. White children are also there, dressed and walking with well-dressed white women holding gifts in their hands. As the car continues on, it passes a set of train tracks to enter the West-side of Dayton. The setting is immediately changed, and the place looks run down, and all the people walking are black and poorly dressed. Some of the black people are dressed in General Motors uniforms, and the children are outside enjoying themselves, throwing snowballs and playing football in the snow.

The Black Cadillac pulls up to a studio, and Robert Ward gets out, looking like a superstar with his guitar case having a big "R" on it, written in rhinestones. Robert pimp walks into the rehearsal studio. The inside of the studio is similar to an old vintage rehearsal studio, and Marshall is at the table, talking to Cornbread, looking pissed off. Satch goes to open the door for Robert, and Robert walks in. Marshall jumps up and heads straight for Robert, angry at him. "You late again! And you missed that show Saturday; I told you I needed that money to pay my rent!" Robert, unafraid, looks Marshall up and down and says, "I don't give a FUCK! I can be as late as I want to be! This my shit! Marshall doesn't back down, "It shows... you always fucking late or not showing up at all! Look, I'm tired of this bullshit, I quit!" Marshall, angry, walks towards the door and Cornbread grabs him. "C'mon, Jones, let it go!" Robert pushes Cornbread out the way, and Marshall and Robert are face to face. Robert says, "You better shut the fuck up before I whoop that ass! Marshall stands there, not being afraid of him and says, "FUCK YOU! Ain't nobody scared of you!"

Marshall takes a swing, punching Robert in the face. Robert barely moves, Pee Wee puts his head down in shame, and Satch shakes his head. Robert punches Marshall, knocking him to the ground, and he jumps on Marshall, punching him in the face, busting Marshall's nose and splitting his lip, causing blood to cover part of his face. Cornbread and Satch grab Robert off of Marshall and hold him back. Pee Wee helps Marshall up, spitting and whipping blood from his mouth, "That's it! Fuck this motherfucker and this band! I'm through with this shit!" Marshall stands with his face covered in blood, facing Robert and looking mad, "I see you still mad... what the fuck you gon' do then?" Marshall stands still and says, "I'm not going to do shit... I quit!"

Robert, seeing Marshall's seriousness, lunges towards Marshall, but Satch grabs Robert. "Hold on, Robert!" Robert tries to attack Marshall again, but Marshall stands firmly in his position. Robert gives Marshall a cold stare, then says, "What!? Get the fuck out then!" Pee Wee, helping bloody Marshall, puts his handkerchief over Marshall's face to wipe and stop the bleeding. Pee Wee, mad as hell, gets up in Robert's face saying, "Listen, motherfucker! After all the thirty-one nighters, two record deals, you just don't get it! Man, I quit too!" Robert being a whole ass, says, "Whatever, I can replace the two of you... Satch?" Satch, now standing by himself, pauses, making a decision based on his moral compass and says, "Pee Wee's right! We done had three songs on the radio, and you still fuckin' up. I'm out!" Satch goes to help Pee

Wee with Marshall, and Pee Wee says, "Look man...the way you talk to the band, is fucked up! The way you treated Marshall is really fucked up! That's not what we're about, man! You've walked off the stage, and from us, for the last time, motherfucker!" Robert looks at everyone, but they all have serious looks on their faces; then Robert grabs his guitar and pimp struts out the door.

CHAPTER TWO

MUSIC STORE WEST-SIDE DAYTON OHIO - DAY - THE YEAR 1965

Pee Wee walking down Gettysburg Avenue, runs into 28-year-old drummer Greg Webster from Hamilton coming out of the Music Store with a new symbol under his arm. Greg is light-skinned, standing at five foot six inches with an old man personality and smoking a pipe. "Greg, what's up, my brother? The two slap five hands. "I'm good... say, what's the deal with Robert? Pee Wee's demeanor changes "Fuck Robert! Let me turn you on to something! Remember Marshall and Satch, right?" "Yeah, of course. Pee Wee puts his hand on Greg's shoulder, then continues, "We are putting together our own band! And all we need is a real good drummer and guitar player." Greg responds immediately, "I'm in! And man, I know a real good guitar player." Pee Wee puts up his hand, gesturing to hold on. "You say this cat is cool, right? Cause we been through some bullshit with Robert." Greg smirks, already knowing the story.

"He's ain't like that, I promise. His name is Leroy Bonner, but he goes by Sugarfoot." Pee Wee plays it cool, not letting on that he knows Sugarfoot. "Pee Wee, he's playing at the 5100 club tonight; you should go check him out." Pee Wee replies, "I'm gonna do that. Here, take my phone number and address." Greg and Pee Wee exchanged information, slapped each other five and parted ways afterward.

PEE WEE'S HOUSE - DAY - THE FOLLOWING DAY

Pee Wee hears a knock on the door, and goes to the window to see; it's Greg. He opens the door to Greg with a big smile on his face, and Greg walks in smiling too, then he slaps him five. "Pee Wee, what's going on, my brother? Make yourself at home, you hungry? Cause I got pizza and beer." "Oh, I already ate, but I'll have that beer, though." Pee Wee goes to the kitchen to get the beer and hears Greg talking loud while lighting his pipe. "So, did you go check out that guitar player I told you about?" Pee Wee comes back from the kitchen and goes to hand Greg the beer. Greg, not paying attention, exhales smoke in Pee Wee's face. Pee Wee, fanning smoke, says, "Look, I got to tell you something. When I asked him to join the band, he didn't say no." Greg, smiling, cuts Pee Wee off. "That's good!" Greg stops after seeing Pee Wee smiling while shaking his head in denial. "Why are you shaking your head no?

"He clearly said, and I quote... HELL NO! All in my face." Greg laughs, "What? Why'd he say that?" Pee Wee sits down and faces Greg, "Well, when Robert wouldn't show up for a gig, Foots would sit in, with no problem. We'd be on stage jamming, and the crowd loving it! Then, Robert would randomly show up and make Sugarfoot leave the stage, and that happened many times." Greg starts to laugh, "You're joking, right?" "Fuck no! One time, after Robert showed up and Foots had to hitchhike back to Hamilton, and it was colder than a motherfucker." Greg says, "That is crazy." Greg sits on the couch, facing Pee Wee. "Well, I have a great relationship with him. I met him when he was 15. Did he ever tell y'all he ran away from home when he was 14?" "You serious?" "When I met Foots, he was playing the harmonica and wanted to play the guitar. At that time, I was playing the organ, so I would play chords, and he would follow me, to learn the notes. Cause he couldn't read music." Pee Wee Pee Wee pops open another beer, shaking his head and looking at Greg. "Yeah, man! He stayed with my wife and me like part of the family." Pee Wee lights a joint, inhales, then exhales, still shaking his head in denial. "Damn, that's some heavy shit." Pee Wee hands Greg the Joint, and he drags a puff too. "Yeah, it is, but don't worry, man, I'll go talk to him tonight."

Pee Wee pumps his fist, gesturing yes. "Thanks, Greg. He's a cool brother. We'd love to have him back, he's a great fit for the group."

LEROY "SUGARFOOT" BONNER'S PLACE - LATER

Sugarfoot is practicing a hard guitar part, looking really frustrated while sitting on his couch. He hears Greg's signature drum pattern knock at his door. Sugarfoot reluctantly gets up to open the door without looking. Greg walks in with a big grin on his face, and they slap five. "Foots?" Sugarfoot, being frustrated, replies with a funky attitude, "Hey man, c'mon in." Sugarfoot closes the door after Greg walks in and goes over to the couch. "Say, man, I spoke to Pee Wee earlier."

Sugarfoot keeps his head down and does not look interested at all. "Pee Wee, huh? Man…" Greg interrupts Sugarfoot. "Hold on, hear me out!" Sugarfoot picks up his guitar, still not paying attention. "Man, change the subject. I'm not trying to talk 'bout those cats." Greg puts his hand on Sugarfoot's shoulder. "Listen, Pee Wee told me all about Robert and what went down. But Robert's gone. It's not like that now." Sugarfoot looks up, mad. "Did he tell you the last time Robert showed up, I had to hitchhike home; it was colder than a motherfucker!" Greg starts to Chuckle as he

continues, "Yeah, he told me everything."
Sugarfoot looks into Greg's eyes, seeing how
serious he was, and replies, "I don't know, man, it's
hard to trust them when –" Greg stands up,
interrupting Sugarfoot.

"We've known each other for some time now, right?
Right?" "Yeah, man, but those motherfuckers."
Greg gets up and puts his hand on Sugarfoot's
shoulder, being sympathetic to his past with Robert.
"Robert's out of the band, Pee Wee told me they not
fucking with him at all! Foots, I got your back, you
know I mean that!" Sugarfoot looks "I know... I
know you got my back, but –"

Greg jumps up, gesturing to hold on, "How 'bout
this? If it ain't what I say it is, we both walk! And
you got my word on that!" Sugarfoot pauses,
putting his head down, then Greg bows his head in
defeat, rubbing his head, he turns around. Then, all
of a sudden, Sugarfoot lifts his head and says, "I got
your word. If I walk, you walk?" Greg turns around
with a new zest. "Hell yeah!" Sugarfoot starts to
grin along with Greg, then says, "OK, let's do it."
Relieved, Greg sits back on the couch and smiles
while taking a sip from the bottle of beer. Then
Sugarfoot goes back to practicing on his guitar.

MARSHALL'S HOUSE – NIGHT

Marshall, with his bass in a case, walking up in his driveway to his dark house. As the car he was in, drives off, they honk their horn. As soon as Marshall hits the porch, he sees a yellow notice on the door. It's a notice of eviction. Marshall shakes his head and takes his keys out, and enters the house. Marshall reaches for a light switch, then he turns it on, but nothing happens. He yells, "FUCK!!! The lights too!" Marshall sits on the floor and puts his head down, feeling defeated.

MARSHALL'S HOUSE - DAY

A month later, Marshall and Satch are at Marshall's house. Satch walks up to the door, slapping Marshall five, then shadow boxes Marshall as he is excited to see him. Satch says, "Man, let me look at you, my brother. How you been holding up?" Marshall replies, "Man, just trying to hold things together. Let see if Pee Wee got something?" As Marshall goes to close the door, he sees a car pull up. In the back seat, he sees Sugarfoot along with Greg. Marshall leaves the door open and says, "They just pulled up." Satch stays seated, being as cool as a fan and says, "What, Pee Wee got us some bums, huh, how they look, man?" Marshall, still not letting on, says, "Don't know, but he reminds me of someone, though." Sugarfoot walks through the door first, saying, "Yeah, I'm back! It took a whole lot of Pee Wee's singing and tap dancing. He said y'all need a real guitar player! So you know!" Satch jumps up, excited, "Pee Wee, you smart little motherfucker, come here." Satch runs and grabs Pee Wee, and when he does, a bottle of wine falls from under his coat. Everyone burst out laughing. Satch says, "See, shit didn't change." Then he hugs Pee Wee again, Marshall and Sugarfoot walk over to the side and Greg, right off the bat and says, "What are we going to call the group?" Marshall jumps in and says, "Oh, you guys are serious? GOOD! Cause I'm tired of ducking my landlord! No turning back now! But we got to do it right this time! We gotta make it!"

Pee Wee sees how serious Marshall is and says, "Man, it took some convincing, but we got a band, baby!" Satch seeing Greg is serious; he helps him get the meeting back on track, "OK, y'all hear Greg, what are we gonna call da band?" No one says a thing. Satch points to Marshall, "Marshall, you got a name for everything. Hit me with some!" Marshall, with all eyes on him, blurts out, "Mistic Energy!" Everyone looks at Marshall like he's crazy, then Pee Wee starts to laugh out loud, and everyone joins him. Pee Wee says, "I knew it. I could have bet that's where your brain is at. This one's really special." Sugarfoot jumps in to defend Marshall and says, "Satch, if I asked you, you would have told me some Pimp or some Player shit." Greg puts his hands up and says, "I like the name Players, though." Satch jumps in and says, "Trust me, I wish, but there's a group with that name already, but we all know who's da real playa!" Satch starts to pop his collar. Marshall keeps acting like there is something he wants to say. ~~Pee Wee~~ Pee Wee, watching him, says, "Go head, Marshall. Spit it out."

Marshall, in his most timid voice, replies, "Ohio Players" The band starts to look at each other, then they start to all nod their heads in approval.

CHAPTER THREE

OHIO PLAYERS FIRST PRACTICE SESSION
DAYTON – 1956

The next day after getting hyped up, the band got together for the Ohio Players' first practice.
Everyone is there holding convos while Greg sits at his drum set looking serious. He hits his two sticks together, grabbing everyone's attention. "All right, all right, let's get serious!" Sugarfoot looking over to Greg smiles, and Marshall says, "Welcome back, Foots; it's good to have you here with us, man, and for good this time." Sugarfoot smiling replies, "You cats better not make me regret it." Everyone takes their places with Greg looking at them with a look that could kill. Sugarfoot then starts to check his tuning, but Marshall can see that he is smiling and happy to be there. Then Greg says, "We're gonna form the best band in the world, everyone will wanna copy, to The Ohio Players!" Greg beats his drumsticks together to create the four-count to the Ohio Players' first practice session.

CHAPTER FOUR

SATCH'S HOUSE/ REHEARSAL STUDIO - NEXT DAY

Satch's wife Carolyn is a sexy 25 years old black woman. Carolyn is altering Pee Wee's outfits in the basement, using Pee Wee as a model while Satch watches. In the background, you hear the band playing music. Pee Wee starts to tap his foot to the music. Carolyn, with a straight face, says, "Pee Wee, don't move!" Pee Wee starts to tap his foot to the music upstairs again, and Carolyn sticks him with a needle in his leg "OUCH!! Now you did that on purpose this time." Carolyn shrugs her shoulders, and Satch laughs and says, "Trust me, don't move again. Carolyn smiles, and LEROY (20, Satch's younger cousin) runs by with his hair smoking while yelling on his way out the back door. Satch looking at Leroy like he's crazy, yells, "WHAT THE FUCK?" Leroy starts running through the backyard, jumps the fence and goes next door. He starts banging the door like a mad man. You see Satch, Pee Wee and Carolyn standing outside the backdoor looking at each other, confused. No one answers the door. Then Leroy jumps back over the fence and runs right past them back into the house. Greg comes running downstairs laughing, saying, "ULTRA WAVE STRIKES AGAIN! Not knowing the waters off upstairs!" Greg pauses, hearing Leroy knocking things over upstairs. They all burst out laughing. Greg, in-between laughing, says, "Marshall talking big shit, told Leroy. I like to let mine sit, and boy did he. Man, I swear Leroy's head was on fire, the way it was smoking!" Satch, Pee Wee, Greg and Carolyn run upstairs to the bathroom to see Leroy with his head in the toilet. When Leroy pulled his head out of the toilet, he looked like the Gerber baby. Satch, Greg, Pee Wee and Carolyn start to laugh.

Greg, laughing, walks back into the room where the band is practicing to see Sugarfoot and Marshall practicing so hard they're sweating. Greg, Satch and Pee Wee, hearing this, open the door digging the groove. The three rush to their instruments, joining in to create an amazing sound.

CHAPTER FIVE
HITTING THE ROAD FOR THE FIRST TIME! 1965 WINTER

Judgement Day, the "Ohio Players" have booked their first gig under their new name. The five band members have all worked together for months working on a unique sound and timing. Standing on the curb in front of Marshall's house are Marshall, Pee Wee, Satch and Sugarfoot, dressed to impress. All of a sudden, they see an old beat-up Black 1952 Dodge B-3-B Panel Van with a big Dayton Daily Post Sticker on both sides; the van sounds as bad as it looked. Everyone jumps in last to get in as Pee Wee gestures; he is zipping his mouth shut after a few looks from Satch and Marshall. Greg driving turns to everyone with a big grin on his face looking for approval, and Marshall and Satch both look at Pee Wee as he puts his hands up like he's nothing to say. Just that fast, the Van stall at the stoplight, one light away from the Oakleaf Nightclub. Marshall, Satch and Pee Wee all embraced pause, and Pee Wee blurted out, "And I'm hungry!" This makes everyone in the van start dying, laughing, cutting the tension. Greg starts the van, and as they turn the corner, they see that line is stretched from the back of the club, and it is wrapped around the building. Marshall looks over to Pee Wee, and he is seen praying; Marshall taps Satch, and the two shake their heads, chuckling. As the van parks, Pee Wee jumps out with his horn and heads straight for the door. The band being late, heads straight for the stage to many whispers as they were once known as Robert's band. Not having the time to feel out the audience has Marshall, Pee Wee and Satch on edge. Greg starts to set up his drums, then pauses as he sees everyone seems a little too quiet. Greg calls everyone in a huddle and says, "Look, I didn't come here for this. I'm gon' tell what we gon' do! We gonna form the best band in the world! Everyone will wanna copy, to The Ohio Players!" After that break, you can see and feel the change in energy. The band started to play, and right off the back, the new sound was a hit; everyone loved it. Leaving the stage to many applauded, the band picks up several shows to reclaim the title of Dayton's Hottest Band real fast.

DOWNTOWN DAYTON, DAYTON RIOTS - DAWN - SEPT 1, 1966

The band driving through downtown Dayton in their van sees burning and vandalized buildings, black people, male and female, on the sidewalks with signs that read, "Lester Mitchell was Just Sweeping, No Justice No Peace, Who's next? When will it stop, and Equality Now?" Greg, pissed off,

53

says, "They said it was three white men! C'mon, man, with 60,000 blacks cramped in this area, they would've had to stick out!" Marshall shakes his head in disgust. "I know we gotta do better; Lester Mitchell was the spark that erupted this volcano." Marshall points out the window to the National Guardsmen. "Shit, look at them, looting and rioting, now the National Guardsmen. All this for a senseless killing of a black man." Satch looking like he wants to jump out says, "They shot that brother in his face, with a shotgun while sweeping! Come on! When will shit change?" More fights were breaking out between blacks and cops as the van passes by.

NIGHT CLUB - THE YEAR 1966

Sabrina, 21, a slim foxy dark-skinned young black lady, from Louisiana is there with her Chaperone, who knows Marshall's family. The Chaperone is trying to impress Sabrina, points to Marshall as he just came off the stage to a cheering audience. The Chaperone points at Marshall, "You see that guy over there? I know him; let me take you over to introduce you." They walk over to Marshall, but the Chaperone makes Sabrina wait 5 feet away while he approaches Marshall. The Chaperone walks up to Marshall, saying, "Hey, Marshall, you see that girl over there?" Marshall sees Sabrina smiling and they lock eyes. Marshall ignoring the Chaperone, doesn't hear a word he says and blurts out, "Oh hell no! I gotta meet her."

Marshall then looks at the Chaperone mischievously, "You not gonna introduce me?" The Chaperone gets the drift and sighs, then walks to get her "Sabrina, I have someone I'd like you to meet." Marshall walks up, not taking his eyes off Sabrina and Sabrina not taking her eyes off him. The Chaperone tries to introduce the two, but they pay him no attention mind, "Sabrina, this is Marshall. Marshall, this is Sabrina." Marshall nor Sabrina looks at the Chaperone. Marshall, giving Sabrina a hug, turns his face away and mouthing the word, "thanks to the Chaperone." The two walk off and take a seat. Sabrina opens her mouth, and she has one of the sweetest southern accents, "Hi," Marshall's eyes pop out his head, "Wow, say that again." Sabrina giggles with a smile that will light up any room, "Oh my, that's some serious jamming Marshall. Where y'all learn to play like that?" Marshall sits speechless and transfixed on her accent. "I've been playing for a while, but I'm really digging your accent. Where you from?" Sabrina, blushing, says, "Louisiana." Marshall staring into her eyes, says, "You sound as good as you look," Sabrina starts to blush and says, "You so sweat." Feeling more comfortable, Sabrina takes her sweater off, and Marshall loses it. Marshall grabs

Sabrina's hand, and they walk right past the Chaperone without looking at him and right out the door.

CHAPTER SIX

NIGHTCLUB CANTON, OHIO - NIGHT - SUMMER 1966

At this time, the "Ohio Players" have made a real name for themselves in the state of Ohio. Playing a packed house in Canton, Ohio, Pee Wee and Marshall exit the nightclub through the backdoor to a poorly lit alley to smoke a joint. Pee Wee taps Marshall. "Give me a light." Marshall passes his lighter to Pee Wee, and a young short, and a stocky black man walks up to them, smiling, "Hey man! I just caught y'all set, and damn, you guys good! For real!" Pee Wee lights the joint then exhales the smoke. "Thanks, man, you wanna hit?" Eddie, "Yeah, that shit smells real good! Pee Wee replies, "Thanks, my brother." Pee Wee passes the joint to Eddie. Eddie, after exhaling, hands the joint to Marshall. Pee Wee turns to Eddie, saying, "Where you from?" Eddie, "Canton, I live here. My Name is Eddie Levert." Pee Wee doing all the talking, as usual, says, "This is Marshall and I'm Pee Wee." Eddie replies, "My pleasure, my brother," Pee Wee looks over to Marshall real quick as if something was wrong. "Bruh, I'm wide open!" Marshall stands there looking confused as he missed the joke. Marshall seeing Eddie smiling, shaking his head, says, "What?" Pee Wee frustrated, says, "Pass that shit you holding, man." Marshall laughs and passes it to Pee Wee. Eddie turns to, "Look, I have a group; I want you guys to hit the road with us. We covered Benny Spellman's "Lipstick Traces." It's on the radio, it may be at 28 on the charts, but it's still a hit. Pee Wee stops Eddie. "Hold on; I want the band to hear this! Marshall, grab everybody."

Marshall walks off to get the band, and Eddie exhaling the joint, says, "It's on the radio, it might be 28 on the charts, but it's still a hit! Pee Wee excitedly says, "Shit, top 40!" Marshall, with the rest of the band, returns and Pee Wee introduces everyone. "Aye y'all check it out, this is Eddie" Eddie introduces himself to the band, "Eddie LeVert! I heard you guys play, and I love that shit yall doin'." Eddie extends his hand to introduce himself to everyone. Greg steps in front, showing his authority, "Thanks, man," Eddie, unbothered, goes right into it. "Yeah, I need you on the road with us! Whattaya say, open up for us and be our backup band?" The Ohio Players look at each other. Satch taps Greg as he sees he's not buying what Eddie's selling either. "What do y'all call yourselves?" Eddie proudly replies, "The O'Jays." Greg turning the heat up on the grill, jumps in front of Satch, saying, "Sounds good, but who's paying us?" Eddie looks over to Pee Wee with a smirk, then confidently replies, "Don't worry, I got you guys covered! Since we gon' hit the road, let me show you our tour bus."

Walking out from the alley, Pee Wee and Eddie continue bonding while Satch, Greg and Sugarfoot walk in the back in disbelief. Once street-side, they don't see a bus. So they keep following Eddie, who stops at a station wagon with his arms out. The station wagon's driver and passenger doors said The O'Jays on the sides were written in paint.

Eddie, just as proud as he could be, said, "Well, there she is!" Pee Wee, with both arms out, replies, "OK, where?" Eddie goes to explain he slaps the roof of the station wagon packed with clothes, while Marshall and Pee Wee make silly faces, and Eddie says, "It's wheels, baby." Pee Wee, with both arms extended, says, "But for how long?" The next week both groups are packed in The O'Jays Station-Wagon, and Eddie is making joke after joke roasting his bandmate, Walter. Pee Wee being Pee Wee, jumps right into the thick of it. "Walter, I know you not gonna let him get on you like that?" Marshall and Satch both start shaking their heads, knowing Pee Wee is only five foot two, but he's the loudest and the most outspoken member of the band, and he's liable to say anything. Eddie takes the bait and says, "Pee Wee, you so short, you gotta jump over da cracks in the sidewalk!" Eddie starts

laughing and adds to it, "Ya little motherfucker!"
Pee Wee inhales the smoke from the joint, hearing
Eddie, he chokes and passes it to Satch, who starts
to chuckle, seeing Pee Wee shake his head,
coughing from trying to get his words out "Man,
you so fat... you fell in love and broke it!"
Everyone starts to laugh, and Eddie giving a real
loud fake laugh, then he goes right in, "Yeah! You
so short, we can see your feet in your driver's
license photo!" Everyone starts dying with laughter.
After exhaling, Satch hands the joint over to Pee
Wee, who then passes it to Eddie. The two would
keep us laughing for 200 miles straight. Pee Wee
would normally win the battles but tonight was
Eddie's. Eddie passes the joint to Pee Wee, smiling
and says, "You guys are really cool" Pee Wee says,
"Thanks, man, so are you guys."

After playing their last set, Pee Wee and Satch head
to the group of girls waiting for them. Cutting them
off is a young singer who looks like James Brown
"Hey man, you guys were good, but you'd be ~~shit~~
great with some Bobby Brown in your set!"

Pee Wee looks Bobby up and down, Pee Wee being
shorter, tries to nudge Bobby out the way to see the
young ladies looking at him and Satch. They both
try to ignore Bobby, but Bobby is not going away.
"Listen! I got the moves! And I can sing; people say
I sound like James Brown. Pee Wee starts waving,

trying to catch eye contact with the girl as Bobby is still standing in his way. Pee Wee gives a comment gesturing his view, "You sho look like da motherfucker!" Pee Wee points to the girls waiting behind Bobby. Pee Wee says, "Negro, you see those girls behind you? That's the only brown I'm tryna see right now. You dig?"

CHAPTER SEVEN

PEE WEE & EDDIE, TOUR BUS? - DAWN - SUMMER 1966

Bobby loses his confidence; he bows his head in defeat and turns around, ready to walk off, saying, "Yeah, man, I can dig it." Satch seeing Bobby looking defeated, taps him and says, "Look, the cat you need to talk to is our drummer Greg. He's still on stage" Bobby gets excited and regains his zest. "THANKS!" Pee Wee puts up the peace sign, and they continue towards the girls. Greg, with his back turned, is breaking down his drum kit, putting the symbols in cases, and Bobby walks up to Greg excited and loud. "Excuse me. Your horn player told me to come to see you about joining the band. My name's Bobby." Greg turns around, looking Bobby up and down, then says, "Can you sing?" You see Bobby with a big grin on his face nodding his head in approval, then confidently replies, "I can dance too!" Greg looks him up and down and says, "Can you lift?" Bobby, confused, stands there, "Man, grab that snare, help me clear the stage." Bobby catching on, says, "Yeah, of course." With a big smile on his face, Bobby rushes over to help Greg clear the stage.

CHAPTER EIGHT

LEO'S CASINO - CLEVELAND WINTER NIGHT DEC 30, 1966

Bobby and the band started picking up steam in different regions of the country, touring with The O'Jays. Entering through the Leo Casino doors in Cincinnati is the Godfather of Soul himself, James Brown, and the promoter goes over to him saying, "Mr. Brown, how are you doing?"

James kept walking, really not trying to hear what he had to say, replied, "Great! But my answer is still no." The promoter trying to piss James off says, "You may have said no to da show, that's cool. In fact, we got a guy coming on next, so hot he might replace you!" James stops dead in his tracks along with his entourage and looks at the promoter like he's stupid. James is cocky while replying, "I'm gon' entertain this bullshit! Come on…" James Brown, along with his entourage, walks into the main hall. James takes a seat along with his entourage, and the lights go out.

The band is on stage, ready to play, and Bobby can be seen behind the left curtain, working on staying calm and waiting for his cue. The Emcee Chuck

Jackson walks out on a light stage. "Ladies and gentlemen, we hear this group is so hot! Well, Imma let the music do the talking... THE OHIO PLAYERS!!!" The band starts to play the intro to 'It's A Man's Man's World' by James Brown on the dark stage. On the dark stage, a spotlight appears, and Bobby comes out from behind the curtain, running, then he slides across the stage, stopping in the middle of the stage in front of the drummer, on the beat of the drum. With the spotlight on him, Bobby puts his head down and waits to milk every piece of his moment; then, he slowly lifts his head and belts out the words, "This is a man, world!" The women in the audience go crazy!

Bobby, at the lead, holds the audience spellbound. The women around James are screaming and hollering. The real James Brown, still sitting in the audience, starts to look at the women around him going crazy, and he is not looking happy about it. After the amazing performance, the Emcee Chuck Jackson smiling and clapping, walks over to Bobby on-stage, clapping, "Give it up for the Ohio Players, ladies and gentlemen! Yeah, give it up!" The crowd, mostly women, goes crazy. The Emcee Chuck Jackson, smiling, lets the audience cheer to the promoter's delight in getting James Brown a little hot under his collar. Chuck seeing, he has James' attention, sends the ultimate shot; he puts his hand on Bobby's shoulder then says. "Now, young man, you good, but do you know that the man who inspired your set is in the audience? That's right, ladies and gentlemen, give it up for soul brother number 1, the Godfather of Soul himself! Mr. James Brown! Mr. Brown, please come up on stage!"

James Brown stands up to the praises of the audience, then makes his way on-stage. On-stage, James doesn't waste any time and cues the band to hit it, and the crowd goes crazy. After the show in the station wagon, the band sees a sign that says James Brown is about to perform in twenty min; everyone in the car loses it.

The band is in the room without Sugarfoot, and Greg and Marshall stands up, mad, "Pee Wee's right, we never should've left that gig with The O' Jays. Look at where we are now! Shit! I want us to make it more than anything!" Satch, with his head down, jumps up, and with a monstrous tone, he says, "Chill the fuck out, Marshall!" Greg slams the door and comes in, holding a letter looking mad. "YOU BELIEVE THIS SHIT?! I got this letter saying they canceled all the tour dates." Satch, still hellbent, gets up to grab the letter. "What? Let me see that!" Marshall and Pee Wee jump off the couch. Marshall turns to-Pee Wee, holding his bottle of wine with just one gulp left in it. Marshall, fed up, says, "So back on the roller-coaster, huh? Pee Wee, you ready for that drink?"

Pee Wee takes the bottle to the head and downs the last gulp, then looks over to Satch, saying, "Now, I am! Don't look at me? I play the trumpet." Marshall and Pee Wee leave through the door. Satch turns to Greg and says, "Remember that Ray Charles label situation?" Greg, remembering, gets really excited, "Yeah! Tangerine Records. What about 'em?" "One of the reps sent a letter, saying they want to do a record." Satch reaches down into some letters next to the chair he's sitting in and grabs a letter. Satch hands the letter to Greg. Greg starts to read the letter, and as he reads it, he smiles and grunts in a pleased manner. "THAT'S IT!"

The two walk into the kitchen. Meanwhile, Marshall and Pee Wee are walking on Gettysburg Ave when a Red Cadillac pulls over to the curb, and the window rolls down and hears a voice "Marshall, Pee Wee, right?" Pee Wee never misses an opportunity and says, "Police, pigs, undercover, right?" Johnny Brantley, a 29-year-old white male and a producer, puts the car in park. Then he gets out of the car in a hurry and walks around to Marshall and Pee Wee with his hand stretched out and a big smile. "Man, I'm glad to run into you guys. That address you have on file from Lupine records is wrong." Marshall shakes his hand. "On purpose, what you want?" "I heard some music you guys worked on while you were in New York. I think y'all got something special."

Marshall and Pee Wee start to sniff their shoulders, then their sleeves, then each other. Johnny scratching his head confused, says, "What you smell?" They both look at each other, then Pee Wee gestures to Marshall go ahead, "BULLSHIT!!!" Pee Wee and Marshall start to laugh, and Johnny standing with a serious face, passes them a business card saying Producer John Brantley for major recording artists and studios. Then, Johnny, in a serious tone, says, "Now that I got your attention, I already drew the paperwork up; hold on!" Johnny walks over to his car and opens the passenger door and grabs a contract out of an envelope, then hands it to Marshall and says, "Oh, you serious!"

Johnny playing it cool, says, "I'll be staying at the Dayton Hotel room 701; I'll be there till Friday." Marshall and Pee Wee both, at the same time, say, "Tomorrow!?" Johnny being arrogant, puts his sunglasses on and says, "It's Thursday already? OK, so let me know what you guys think?"

Johnny gives them a straight look, nods his head, then he goes into his car and drives off. Johnny looks at Marshall and Pee Wee looking at the card in the rear-view mirror, and he pumps his fist, then slaps the dashboard yelling "YES!!!" Marshall and Pee Wee walk in the door to see Greg and Satch sitting down, acting real funny, being silent and smiling at them. Pee Wee pops open his bottle of wine and says, "For the unforgotten…" instead of pouring the wine on the floor, Pee Wee tilts his head and pours it in his mouth. You see Satch shaking his head in disgust. Marshall lets the silence get to him and says, "What y'all done went crazy! Why y'all smiling at us?" Greg looks at Satch. "You wanna tell em, or should I?" Satch smiling, calmly replies, "They don't look ready." Greg lights his pipe and blows the smoke towards Marshall and Pee Wee as they stand there. Pee Wee, pissed off, goes to say something, and Marshall gestures to Pee Wee to wait and doesn't say anything. Greg, still smoking his pipe, exhales, then says, "Nah, make 'em suffer." Greg takes a second drag and exhales the smoke.

"Satch, you know what, go ahead tell 'em. Satch stands up, "WE GOT A DEAL PLAYER!"

Marshall looks at Pee Wee and shakes his head, gesturing in denial. Satch and Greg look puzzled as Marshall and Pee Wee don't look excited at all. Then Marshall whips out the contract, and they both smile real big then Pee Wee gestures to Marshall to take the floor, and he yells, "WE GOT ONE, TOO, BUT IN WRITING, where's your contract, huh?

Huh?" Satch's and Greg's jaws drop, then Greg gets up, reaching for the contract as Marshall extends his hand to give it to him. Greg gets the contract and starts to read it while Satch stands over near him. Pee Wee passes the wine to Marshall as they act cocky. Greg looks at Satch and, in a low tone, says, "it looks real." The door opens, and Sugarfoot walks in looking mad, "That's some bullshit! They dropped all da shows!" Sugarfoot looks at everyone's faces, and you see they're not taking him seriously, and they're smiling at him. Sugarfoot catching the vibe, says, "OK, what I miss?" Pee Wee getting the bottle back from Marshall, says, "Two deals, motherfucker!" Pee Wee, drunk, holds the bottle up. Greg, with Satch right over his shoulder, is still reading the contract, and he says, "This looks good. Johnny is the real deal, I heard about him when we was in New York. It's a production contract. That's perfect, along with Tangerine Records now we complete."

Greg snatches the bottle of wine from Pee Wee and takes a drink, then puts it in the air.

TANGERINE RECORDS STUDIO - DAY

The band is escorted by a young intern into the building to see posters and pictures on the wall accompanied by gold records of Ray Charles. As they continue to walk towards the studio, on the walls, they see posters of Ike & Tina and their single "Beauty Is Skin Deep." They also see a poster on the wall of the Raelets and their single "One Room Paradise" Marshall points to the window to look into the studio, and they see Ray Charles recording a record, and everyone's eyes light up. The intern stops at Studio B next door and says, "This way, please." The band walks into the studio, and there is Johnny already waiting on them; sitting at the control board says, "We only have a few hours of time so let's get to it. Take your Gobos, and Bobby go to the mic in the center." Everyone walks over to their Gobo (A partition between musicians), and Bobby walks over to the microphone in the middle. Johnny walks out of the booth, and he is seen pointing at Bobby as he talks to the engineer. Three interns walk in and start to grab little microphones and then start to mic up the band's instruments in their Gobos.

Johnny, outside of the booth, speaks through the crosstalk. "Is everybody ready?" Greg replies, "Let's go."

Then Greg looks at the band and yells to get their attention, "ARE WE READY?" Everyone replies, "Hell Yeah, etc." Johnny, through the crosstalk, says, "Hit it!" Greg looking at the band, says, "On

1." Greg slapping his drumsticks together, counts out loud, "4, 3, 2, 1." The band begins to play A Thing Call Love by the "Ohio Players." Bobby starts to sing with his eyes closed.

Taking a break, Johnny and Greg are sitting in a booth in a nearby diner. Johnny slides a contract across the table, and Greg says, "What's this for?" Johnny replies, "You want to be paid, right?" Greg, looking confused, starts rubbing his forehead and Johnny, seeing this, asks Greg, "Don't you have a lawyer?" Greg timidly replied, "No... is that going to be a problem?" Johnny smiles while saying, "Not for me... but you need one!" Johnny picks up the contract and flips two pages; then he points to a section of the contract saying, "OK, Greg, you see this section, for instance, this is the record split." Greg looking even more confused, says, "SPLIT? Johnny, we all split everything even! We will all receive writing credits as you will be keeping the production." Johnny replies, "I can dig it! Greg, you're a good person; look, I'm going to pull a few strings to see if we can make an album. Compass owes me a favor or two." Greg smiling says, "That sounds good to me, and I'll get a lawyer to look at this contract and get it back to you." The waitress walks to the table with their food and puts it on the table, then she turns to them and says, "Is everything alright?" Greg looks at Johnny and smiles, then turns to the waitress and says, "It's great!"

COMPASS RECORDS STUDIO'S -
AFTERNOON - 1968

The song "It's A Crying Shame by the Ohio Players" plays. Johnny is sitting in the studio by himself, listening to the song on the control board. Then a middle-aged white man in a sharp suit and nice briefcase walks in. He walks up to Johnny with a big smile on his face and his arm stretched out in a handshake gesture. "Mr. Brantley, I presume?" Johnny replies, "Call me Johnny, Mr.?" Walter shakes his hand, saying, "Walter Pepsi, Johnny, I'm here from Capitol Records, and there's a great situation I want to present to you guys. You're their producer, right?" Johnny, not impressed and ready to get back to work, replies, "Walter, Spit it out already." This catches the attention of the band, and Walter says, "Ok, Capitol is willing to offer you guys an album deal. After seeing what you guys did on Trespassing, we think your boys are the right fit for us." Johnny was still looking at Walter, unimpressed, and before Johnny could say something, Walter says, "Hold on before you say something, look at this contract." Walter hands Johnny the contract, and Johnny sees the huge dollar amount, and Johnny smiles, saying, "This will work; boy would this work." Johnny smiles at Walter, and he stretches his hand, and they shake hands laughing. The band walks into the studio seeing Johnny and Walter slapping five and looking really happy. Greg, knowing about the meeting, says, "Johnny, what's shakin'?" Johnny replies, "Well, I'll let Walter spread the good news." The band turns to Walter, "Hi, I'm Walter Pepsi, and I'm from Capitol Records, and we want to sign you boys. Label and I think you're ready to work on an album" The band with Bobby starts to get excited and starts to slap fives. Then Walter says, "Now hold on, before you get excited, let me really get your blood bubbling. Check the advance you guys are getting." Greg looks at the amount, then looks over to Johnny, who shakes his head and puts his thumb up. Greg, with the band standing over him as he points to the number, gets excited. Greg trying to play it cool, says, "Looks like we got a deal." Everyone in the room congratulates each other.

TOWNHOUSE IN BUFFALO NY – 1968

Greg is in the van outside, Greg is heard and seen blowing the horn. As the band comes outside, Marshall is the first to walk over, followed by the rest of the band. Marshall running to the van first, yells, "SHOTGUN!" Marshall gets in the front passenger seat, and Pee Wee opens the side door of the van, and everyone gets in. Satch slams the door, and it doesn't close; he does it again, slamming it harder. Greg smirks, looking back, and he says, "Oh yeah, you got to close it from the outside. Marshall, close the door for me." Marshall looks at Pee Wee, and before Pee Wee could say anything, Greg says, "Pee Wee, don't say nothing, I see you ready to start your bullshit." Pee Wee being as charismatic as he could be, says, "OK, boss." Marshall slams the door and gets back in the van, and they drive off. Greg smiling while looking at everyone, says, "And she drives great, come on, just seven-fifty. Even you got to admit this is a great deal, right?" Pee Wee gestures that his mouth is zipped shut, and Marshall looking at him, laughs. Then Marshall replies, "You told him don't say nothing right (chuckling)." Satch giving directions, points left, and says, "Make the next right here, Greg."

Halfway through the turn, the van shuts off. "Let me pull over and crank her up!" Greg looks in the rearview mirror while turning and sees Pee Wee shaking his head looking right back at him. Greg, in a slow crawl, pulls the front of the van to the curb then tries to crank it again and again. Then Greg gets out with Satch, and Greg pops open the hood to see smoke and antifreeze leaking from the bottom. Satch tries to whisper to Marshall, now standing next to him, "Only seven-fifty, right?" From inside

the van, everyone hears Pee Wee yell, "ONLY
SEVEN-FIFTY, RIGHT? NOBODY BETTER
NEVER LET THIS MOTHERFUCKER PICK
ANOTHER VAN"

Everyone starts to laugh. Later that night, after
getting a hose replaced, the band hits the road with
Marshall at the wheel, going through a one-light
town deep in the backwoods of Kentucky in 1967!!!
Pee Wee is holding a half-empty bottle of wine, and
being Pee Wee is getting on anyone that he felt like
says, "Man, your momma so stupid..." Marshall,
nervous, interrupts Pee Wee while looking in the
rearview mirror and he sees flashing lights behind
them while driving.

In a hurry, Marshall says, "SHIT... Hide the weed,
man, we getting pulled over." The van pulls over,
and Satch rushes to stash everything, and Pee Wee
takes the last of the wine straight to the head. The
officer, a tall 60-year-old white man with a heavy
country twang, walks up so slow he might as well
have crawled as nervous as Marshall was because of
the time and situation. The officer taps on the glass
with his nightstick for Marshall to roll the window
down, saying, "License and Registration." Marshall
starts to check his pocket but realizes that he left it
at the townhouse in Buffalo, NY. Marshall replies,
being as sympathetic as he could, "I don't have it,
sir, but I am a licensed driver from Ohio." The

Officer pulls his gun from the holster and points it at Marshall, saying, "You don't have your license? Step out of the vehicle and put your hands behind your back." While searching Marshall, the officer looks in the van and says, "Now somebody better have a license?" Satch shows his license, and the officer says, "Mr. Satchell follow me to the station." The officer slaps handcuffs on Marshall, then he puts Marshall in the patrol car, and they drive off. The band, with Satch at the wheel, follows them. Pulling up, they see an all-in-one, Local Jail/Courthouse; this building looked old and racist. The band minus Marshall is sitting in the van in the parking lot, watching the officer walk Marshall towards the empty-looking building with Marshall in cuffs.

Marshall and the officer enter the building while the rest of the band watches, and Greg says, "Let's put some bread together to get Marshall out." Greg Starts adding up all their money as he uses his hat as the "Free Marshall pot." Greg looks over to Satch in the driver's seat and says, "OK, one hundred and seventy-five dollars, nobody's holding out... right?" Satch rolls down the driver's window to smoke a cigarette, and as Greg looks up from counting the money, Marshall is seen walking through the front doors towards the van. As Marshall gets close to the van, he looks at Satch and quietly says, "Let's go,

I'll drive." Satch, smiling being the gangster that he is thinking they're making a break for it, smiles at Marshall then says, "I'll start the van." Satch jumps in the back, and Marshall gets behind the wheel and drives off. Bobby, grabbing his things and sounding scared as hell, says, "Let me out, you motherfuckers are crazy!" Everyone ignores Bobby, and for maybe thirty miles, everyone could hear a pin drop. Pee Wee being Marshall's best friend, steps in as Marshall is not talking; he leans over the back of the driver's seat and says, "What the hell happened, Marshall?" Marshall playing it real cool, says, "Nothing." Greg loses it, his eyes pop right out of his head, and he yells, "WHAT?" Sugarfoot, seeing Greg losing it, joins in and says, "Marshall, don't give me no bullshit; what the fuck you got me in!"

Pee Wee, seeing both of them grabbed their bags again from under their seats. Pee wee puts his hand up gesturing to wait, then Bobby zips his coat up and tries to get up to jump out, but Pee Wee watching him, pushes him back in his seat and says to Bobby with a straight face, "Man, sit the fuck down!" Pee Wee goes back over to Marshall and says, "Marshall, what the hell happened?" Marshall lets go of the straight face and smiles as Pee Wee is now in between the front seat right up in his face. Then Marshall says, "The officer took me in there, and I was scared, you dig?" Bobby says, "hell yeah!" "Man, I was scared, he walked me into the police station. I almost shit a brick! He took me down this long-ass hallway, then into this courtroom and said to have a seat. I was like, have a seat? Man, I was looking for the fuckin' door, you dig?" Pee Wee, being engulfed in the conversation, hurries Marshall along by saying, "Then what happened?" Marshall, with a big grin, starts to explain, continuing with the story, "He sat me down in the courtroom, and then walked off into a side door, leaving me there by myself. My legs were shaking so bad; I thought I was tap dancing. So I started rubbing my legs as fast as I could, but they wouldn't stop shaking! I was scared, I didn't want them to think I was gonna run, so they could beat my ass. Then all of a sudden, the same cop that locked me up came out wearing a Judge's robe. Almost in unison, every confused person says, "Huh!" Marshall, the great storyteller, goes back to it "He had on a judge's robe with a mean face, then he went to the bench, and hit the hammer. I was so nervous I almost passed out. The next thing I knew, he said, "Ten Dollars." And told me to pay the bailiff on my way out the door." Pee Wee, the big little brother in this relationship, slaps Marshall in the back of his head while saying, "What the fuck!" Everyone in the van bust out laughing.

Still on the road, hours later, Marshall is driving through a snowstorm, wiping the windshield from inside to see on I 78 headed to Buffalo, NY. Pee Wee, now in the passenger seat, says, "Hey Marshall, you OK?" Marshall, still wiping the window with a rag, replies, "Yeah, just that this snow makes it hard to see, and it's slippery out here." Pee Wee smirks with a devilish grin and says, "You need something? Marshall catching the drift, replies, "Hell yeah, roll something up." Satch half-sleep jumps right in the convo. "What you waiting for, man." Just then, two motorcycles fly by recklessly on the snowy road shaking the van; Marshall points and says, "SHIT, did you see that!" Pee Wee rolling barely looks up, then replies, "Fuck em, they'll be all right." About a mile ahead, Marshall and the band sees one of the two motorcycles parked in the middle of the road, and the other one smashed inside the back of a cargo van. Marshall seeing this hit the brakes as hard as he could, stopping their van within inches of the cyclist smashed into the cargo van. Then Marshall, hearing a loud truck horn, looks in the rearview mirror to see that the eighteen-wheeler truck behind them is not able to stop. Marshall seeing this, yells, "Y'ALL HOLD ON! Everyone braced themselves, and the truck slowly bumped and pushed the van into the motorcyclist, breaking his leg. Pee Wee, drunk and high, starts overreacting, as usual, jumps out of the driver's window without touching a thing. Pee Wee out of the van and outta his mind starts to go bananas in the snow saying "THAT'S IT! I'M DONE, I'M GOING HOME! That motherfucker jumped all the way in the back of the van. And we done broke this motherfucker's leg! I quit! Take me home, you know what! fuck it; I'll walk, just send me my shit!" Pee Wee walks off in the snowstorm.

CHITLIN CIRCUIT, ATLANTA, ROYAL PEACOCK'S BATHROOM 1967

Pee Wee and Satch are in the bathroom, in two different stalls having sex with two pretty young black women. Out of Pee Wee stall, a young black woman yelling while moaning, "OH MY GOD... Pee Wee. Oh, oh, oh yes! YES!!!" Satch behind Young Black Woman #2 both start shaking their head in the stall, then he goes back to hitting it from behind. The music stops, and the announcer says, "UP NEXT IS ONE OF MY PERSONAL FAVES, THE OHIO PLAYERS!!!!" Satch bangs the partition between stalls. Pee Wee, getting frustrated, replies, "One minute!" Satch, distracted, says, "OK, make it two, you throwing me off."

The girl shakes her head then Satch slaps her on her ass. Young Black Woman #1 lets out a loud moan of satisfaction. Then they hear the bathroom door knock loudly and Marshall yelling, "SATCH

COME ON, MAN, YOU GOT THE KEYS! WE
NEED OUR STUFF!"

Satch and Young Black Woman #2 walks out of the
stall, fixing their clothes. Satch ready says, "Come
on, Pee Wee!" Pee Wee hearing the loud second set
of knocks Marshall's making, bursts out of the stall
with his pants at his ankles. Young Black Woman
#2, seeing Pee Wee is hung like a horse, her eyes
pop out of her head. Then she says, "Pee Wee, my
ass! Girl, you alright in there?" Pee Wee smiled,
then pulled up his pants, and Young Black Woman
#2 kissed Satch on his cheek and shook her head at
Pee Wee. Then she walks into the stall to help her
friend while Satch and Pee Wee leave in a hurry
fixing their clothes. The band is in their places, and
there is dead silence in the room, and a man in the
audience yells, "WHAT THE FUCK Y'ALL
WAITING FOR!" The two young women that were
with Pee Wee and Satch in the stalls put their hands
up in the front row. The band starts to play
Neighbors by the "Ohio Players." Greg starts
slapping his drumsticks together, and Satch and Pee
Wee start to play their horns while Greg hits the
snare creating the snapping sound. Bobby and
Marshall work the audience with tambourines,
slapping them to Greg's snare drum, and the
audience starts to clap along. The two young black
ladies dancing, looking straight towards the stage,

smiling at Pee Wee and Satch in a real devilish manner. Bobby starts to sing, and his voice drives the girls crazy while they do the latest dances from The Boogaloo, The Mashed Potato, and The Twist. Bobby is singing at the end of the stage, and Bobby has ten girls dancing, trying to keep his attention while singing. Bobby gets hit smack in his face with an extra-large pair of panties, and when he looks up, it's a big Mama with her hand in the air. Big Mama starts to dance up a storm, and the crowd goes wild. Bobby signals to the band to stop, then Bobby holds up the extra-large pair of panties and says, "Girl, these some big draws... and I like it!" Big Mama smiles and puts her hand up in the air, then Bobby turns to the band and says, "Y'all think they're ready for one more?" The crowd starts to chant, "More, More!" Bobby working the crowd, says, "Y'ALL READY!

The band starts to play what they did not know would soon be their first single, "A Thing Called Love," by the "Ohio Players." Bobby starts to sing, and at the chorus, Satch and Pee Wee step up to play the horn parts to the delight of the audience, who begin to cheer. Then two guys sandwich big Mama while she holds her hand in the air, and the crowd goes crazy. After the show, backstage in an office, Greg and Satch are talking to a mean-looking black man with a nasty scar on his left cheek. Satch stands behind Greg, and behind Satch is a huge black man guarding the locked door. The promoter's wife sits behind his desk, having wads of cash on it. Satch mad as a motherfucker blurts out, "We did the motherfuckin' show, now pay us!" Greg puts his hand up, gesturing Satch to chill out. "NOW HOLD ON, SATCH!"

"You telling me we not getting paid?" The Promoter's wife pulls a gun out from her husband's desk drawer and puts it on top of the desk. While she's looking at Satch with an evil look in her eyes, she says, "That's right! Keep a muzzle on your puppy!" Satch is about to say something, but Greg looks at him. The promoter's wife gets up with the gun, and she is a tall sexy dark-skinned black woman, and she says, "I'm getting bored, let me out. I got to use the bathroom." Marshall and Bobby are walking up to the back door by way of the alley where Greg and Satch are. Marshall walking with his duffel bag, stops and says, "Hold on, Bobby, let me put these stink ass clothes down before we walk in there to get this money."

Marshall puts the bag down at the side of the door and goes to knock on the door, but the door opens due to security kicking a drunken man out the back of the club. Marshall rushes to catch the door, holding it, so it appears close. Then he opens it to see Satch and Greg looking mad; Marshall puts his bag to hold the door. Marshall holds the door open, catching Satch's attention, and Bobby runs to the car with the keys. Satch seeing the door open takes his chance; he grabs a wad of cash off of the table and runs past the security guard now sitting on the couch.

Greg follows him and Marshall and Bobby run behind them. The promoter's wife yells, "GET THEM MOTHERFUCKERS!!!" The security guard pulls his gun out and starts to run after them but trips over Marshall's bag. Causing the security guard to fall, making him involuntarily fire his pistol. The shot just misses the promoter's wife by inches, and she loses it "YOU BIG FOR NOTHING, PIECE OF SHIT! OH, I WISH YOU DID…" As the car passes with everyone ducked down, they see the promoter's wife cursing the security guard out.

DOWNTOWN PITTSBURGH AT AN HOTEL

To get to their rooms, the players have to use an old-fashioned manual elevator with no back wall. Before the elevator doors close, three big white men get in the elevator looking like trouble. One of the big white guys standing with his back to the open back wall of the elevator as they ascend acts completely oblivious to it and stands with his hands looking tough. Pee Wee, drunk and always outspoken, noticing it points to the wall, says, "Hey man, be careful, don't get too close, you may get hurt." The big white guy standing on the other side looking down at Pee Wee, literary then he says, "Shut the fuck up, ain't nothing going to happen to him when he's with us!"

Marshall and Greg both look at Pee Wee like let it go, and Pee Wee says, "Well, fuck it then!" Nothing is said the rest of the ride. The three white boys get off on the third floor. The elevator door closes and reopens on the fourth floor.

The elevator door opens, and the three white guys are standing there, blocking the doorway. Marshall seeing this, says, "Hey man, what's going on?" The white guys pounding their fist, gives them their answer and out of nowhere, Pee Wee jumps in front of Marshall and says, "Hold on! I'll break this shit up!" Pee Wee busts right through the three big white guys with force. The big three white guys get scared and leave, seeing Pee Wee acting like he got something.

Marshall and Greg are in the room explaining what just happened to Satch and the rest of the band, and Pee Wee comes back. Everyone in the room gets quiet, and Satch gives Marshall a look, and he walks up to Pee Wee, and he says, "Why you took off, man?" Pee Wee, not trying to hear it tries to walk by, but he looks over to the couch and sees some ladies. Pee Wee, with a straight face trying to impress the ladies, says, "What? I knew they would think I went for something; it worked, right?"

Marshall is pissed off as Pee Wee keeps brushing him off and says, "Whatever, you shouldn't have left us." Pee Wee, still in his ego, says, "Man, it will be ok," Pee Wee turns to the ladies while pointing to a bottle of champagne sitting on the coffee table and says, "This way, ladies." Pee Wee starts pouring glasses for the ladies while Marshall and Greg shake their heads at him.

The band is with the three ladies in the hotel room dancing, drinking and smoking. Then Greg at the door says, "Hey y'all, I'll be back. I have to go to the van to grab something."

Pee Wee, dancing with one of the girls, lets her go and grabs Greg's arm, looking concerned, and he says, "Them guys might be out there; I'm going with you!" Greg, not sounding too thrilled, replied, "Cool man, come on." Greg and Pee Wee leave the band and the girls and behind.

Greg and Pee Wee are in the elevator, and the doors open to the lobby, and the three white boys are waiting for them. The biggest one seeing them getting off the elevator, yells, "THERE HE GO!" His eyes glowing with malevolence, they hurry over to Greg and Pee Wee from both sides. Greg focused on the biggest one, did not notice the sneaky short white guy sneaking behind him. Greg gets his clock cleaned, getting hit from behind, and he falls back and becomes slightly unconscious. The biggest one rushes over and starts kicking Greg. One of the kicks brings him to his senses, and Greg jumps to his feet, swinging. Greg punches the small sneaky white guy in the nose, causing blood to drip, and then punches the biggest one in the face knocking him down. Greg looks over and sees the other white guy getting the best of Pee Wee on the steps hitting and kicking him in the head. Greg rushes over, and tackles the white guy off of Pee Wee. Then he quickly grabs two bottles to go back in the fight; by the time Greg looks over, he sees Pee Wee's gone. Before anything else could happen, Pittsburg Police Officers break them up.

The officers pull the white guys to the side first to ask them what happened and from their side. Greg sees the white guys pointing, and the small sneaky one pointing at them yells, "HE STARTED IT!"

The white officers standing with the three white guys start looking over towards Greg like they took the side of the three white guys. Without saying a word to Greg and just feeling it in his guts, the officers tried and convicted him. It's like the gavel slammed and the verdict was out, Greg was in the wrong the officers start to approach Greg. Pee Wee running down the stairs with Marshall starts to lose it seeing Greg going in cuffs, and he says, "Hell no, let him go, they started it!" The officers surrounding him roughly put him in handcuffs, causing a commotion as Marshall and Pee Wee, and onlookers protest these rough actions taken against Greg. Hearing the commotion, the hotel manager rushes over to Greg, Pee Wee and Marshall's, defense, saying, "Hold on, what going on here?"

The white police officer walks over, chewing his gum with his mouth open, and he says, "Well, this negro…" The manager puts his hands up, gesturing to stop; while pointing to Pee Wee, the hotel manager says, "Now hold on, I asked him." Pee Wee, feeling more confident about things, starts to explain, "We came downstairs to get something from the van, and those guys jumped on us and were kicking my friend, and the other one was holding me down on the steps.

They would have killed me if we didn't fight back!" The hotel manager takes charge of the situation and says, "Listen... these guys have been coming here for years, and I never had any trouble out of them. Look, I'm going to tell you what you're gonna to do. Those three are going to get out of here. They need to leave now!" The police reluctantly remove the three white guys telling them they need to leave.

BACKSTAGE CLUB 611 DAYTON, OHIO - NIGHT - SPRING 1968

Bobby is backstage in a local nightclub talking to a very pretty little light-skinned black girl. Bobby being so loud, everyone can hear him while the other band members get ready to go on-stage. Bobby speaking loudly and being as animated as could be, starts grandstanding, "Say, baby, why you want the old thing when you can have the new and improved, huh?" Marshall and Greg watching both smirks, and Marshall says, "Bobby's a star; we gonna make it big!" The door knocks really loud, and everyone pauses, then Greg goes to open it. Rushing in comes the LOCAL POLICE and MILITARY MP's with a picture of Bobby. They walk straight over to Bobby, slapping the cuffs on him. Greg stands in front of them, trying to stop them from leaving with Bobby. "Now, hold on! What's this about?" A big white MILITARY MP walks up to Greg and, speaking with a thick country accent, says, "This boy's a draft dodger! You wanna take his place? Now outta my way!" Greg reluctantly moves out of the way, and they leave with Bobby in cuffs.

CHAPTER NINE
SATCH'S HOUSE - NIGHT - WINTER 1967

Greg's at the table, holding a letter in his hand with his other hand on his head while the band sets up to practice. Sugarfoot and Marshall are at their usual spot at the chess table, and Sugarfoot, looking depressed, says, "Since Bobby got drafted to Vietnam, we still haven't found a singer to get back on the road." Marshall, moving his chess piece, replies, "We got to do something fast; my bills are stacking up, fast!" Greg walks over, looking even more depressed, "Hey y'all, I got a letter to share with y'all." Everyone stops what they are doing and comes over, concerned by the look on Greg's face. Pee Wee walks up, putting his arm on Greg's shoulder. "What's up? It sounds serious?" Greg was speaking real soft and tried to get it out, but no one understood him. Satch walks from behind and takes the letter from Greg to read it. The first thing Satch says is, "FUCK!" Satch pausing for a brief moment with his hand on his head, sighs, then he says, "Bobby got shot!"

Marshall angrily knocks the pieces off the chessboard; then, the room gets real silent. Marshall, angry, stands up and says with conviction, "Losing another singer ain't easy, and yeah, we found that out right away! With Robert and the Untouchables, we had been disciplined to the point that every breath he took and every little nuance of his act, we had him! We were just that tight of a unit. So stepping out with a new lead singer was hard, and it may not be our last time. Brothers, we in too deep in this lifestyle, ain't no turning back now!!! A real player never gives up on his dream anyway, so giving up is not an option!" Everyone looks at Marshall, confused as he never spoke to the band like this, but within seconds everyone's starts to cheer him on.

NEW JERSEY ISLEY BROTHERS RECORDING STUDIO.

The band is at the studio to record new material. John Brantley, the producer, has an idea "Hey guys, would you mind playing behind a singer I got?" Pee Wee jumps right up. "What?" Satch enforcing what Pee Wee said, says, "We don't wanna play behind people, man. We the Ohio Players, Jack!" Johnny pleads his case, "At least listen to her; she's real good." Greg stands in the center of everyone to get their attention, and he says, "Let's hear her first." Johnny, with his head down, lifts it up and smiles. "Great, let me just go and get her."

Johnny leaves and returns with a mildly attractive white woman looking very nervous. She looks over to Johnny as everyone is already in their places and says, "Are you sure? I don't want to cause you any inconvenience." Johnny playing the bigshot, waves his hand, gesturing no problem, then he says, "NONSENSE, let's let them hear your wonderful voice." Johnny points to the vocal booth and turns his head, acting serious as if he doesn't want to hear anything. The Woman looks at the band, and they all shrug their shoulders. The Woman goes into the vocal booth. Johnny acting like he wants to show off a new toy, cues the band, "OK on 1, 3, 2, 1." The band begins to play an instrumental, and about five bars into the song, the Woman completely freezes, and Johnny, through the crosstalk, says, "Is everything alright?"

The Woman standing in the Booth speaks into the microphone to Johnny, saying, "I don't know, maybe it's the song?" Johnny sends the band a request through the crosstalk "Hey guys, can you play a ballet something real slow?" The band begins to play the ballet, and the shy woman goes to the microphone and sings. The woman couldn't sing; she sounded like shit. When she starts moaning, trying to harmonize, Marshall loses it. "FUCK, I can't take it!" Everyone stares (like chill out) at

Marshall, and Marshall catching himself and changes the subject.

"Oh shit! This is a nice place; who owns this?" Johnny replies, "The Isley Brothers." Pee Wee helping smooth it out jumps right in. "They here?" Johnny gestures no through the glass window. Then the band starts to play, and the woman begins to sing. Everyone tries not to make eye contact with Pee Wee as he makes fun of her singing.

The session ends, and she smiles as she sees Johnny walking over, clapping proudly, and Pee Wee joins in whistling while clapping, and the band plays along. "What I tell you, uh? Isn't she something?" Greg smiling says, "She something." Johnny excitedly puts his thumb up with his arm around the singer and walks out. Pee Wee, right behind the door, closes it, then he checks to see if the coast is clear then says, "What the fuck was that? She sounded like Tiny Tim!" The band members burst out laughing. Greg looks at Satch, saying, "Satch, you know what that's about? She must be good at somethin'."

Everyone starts to laugh, and Marshall stands up with a serious face and says, "She needs to shut the fuck up!" This causes the band members to lose it, being unable to stop laughing. Pee Wee goes in, clowning the girl's voice (Moaning offbeat.)

Marshall trying to change the narrative says, "Listen on a serious note when Johnny come back, I'm going to talk to him cause this ain't going nowhere fast." Johnny walks back into the studio to dead silence. "Why's everybody so quiet?" Marshall gets up to say something, but Greg jumps up quickly, trying to stop Marshall. Greg, with his hand on Marshall's chest, looks him dead in the eyes, but this time it doesn't work, and Marshall, in a deep low tone, says, "Greg, with all due respect, get the fuck out of my way, JOHNNY, WHAT THE FUCK WAS THAT?

I didn't bring this situation to this band with this bullshit in mind!" The band members stand in amazement as they have never seen Marshall this serious. Johnny, with his arms out, pleads his case "Marshall, I'll get you guys some A-Listers. Look how about this, I've got a badass singer, now you know I've worked with everybody, Jimi ... oh and boy do I have the right guy for you guys. Johnny gets a piece of paper and starts to write Johnny looking Marshall in the eyes. He hands Marshall a paper then says, "Joe Harris, this young guy is amazing; go check him out this Sunday."

NEW YORK CITY, CHURCH - DAY - SPRING 1968

Marshall and Pee Wee walk into a huge church in Harlem. Marshall and Pee Wee are in an empty church's lobby to check out a singer named Joe Harris. Pee Wee, pissed, starts to whine about the current situation. "What we doing here, Marshall?" Marshall, tired of the whining, says, "We're about to lose everything! We need a singer bad! How long you think Compass is gonna keep us around bullshiting. Look, if he's as good as they say he is, we gotta get him!"

Marshall opens the door to the main hall, and you see the choir on stage. The choir stands assembled and ready, the choir director gives his signal. A female dancer runs out and starts dancing as the church band plays "This Little Light of Mine" by Clara Ward. Then a slim framed, 5-foot 9 inches Joe Harris comes out and sings and boy did he. Joe captivates everyone in the audience. Marshall and Pee Wee stand to their feet with the whole congregation cheering and singing along. Marshall, feeling Joe's singing, says, "That boy can sing. We need him like yesterday."

A young lady dancing and shaking her ass locks eyes with Pee Wee, then smiles. Pee Wee, dumbfounded by her beauty, answers, "Yeah." The young lady continues dancing to Pee Wee's delight; then, she smiles at Pee Wee, giving him a very inviting look. Pee Wee heads for the front row, and as he starts to walk off down the isle, Marshall grabs his arm and says, "We ain't here to pick up chicks." Pee Wee looking at Marshall like he's stupid, replies, "You know a better place?" Pee Wee walks off towards the young lady, and Marshall puts his head down. After the service, Marshall is talking to Joe, who is excited and says, "You serious! I heard y'all play up in Harlem, y'all no joke." Marshall seeing he has him, plays it cool "Thanks, Johnny told us bout you. He said you'd fit some of the songs we have, and he's right!" Joe excitedly says, "Man, if y'all serious, count me in." Pee Wee comes over, slapping a piece of paper with the girl's number on it. Then he stretches his hand to Joe, introducing himself. "Pee Wee! You sound good, man, well you in?" Joe, really not feeling Pee Wee's vibe, tries to play stern. "Yeah,

as long as you say it is what it is. Man, I ain't got no time for nonsense.

MARSHALL'S HOUSE - MORNING

Marshall returning home from New York, sees a yellow cab parked outside of his house with his children in the backseat. The trunk is open and has luggage in it. The front door opens as Marshall gets out of his yellow cab with his luggage; you see Sabrina coming out of the house with a suitcase, and Marshall puts his luggage down and runs up to her, but she keeps walking. "You not even gonna talk to me?" The driver gets out to help with the bag with his hands up, gesturing he doesn't want any problems. He takes the suitcase and puts it in the trunk, and closes it. Sabrina looks in the cab as the children start to cry, and Marshall's son starts to yell, "I WANT MY DADDY!!!"

Marshall tries to block her from going into the cab, and Sabrina looks at Marshall with a look of disgust and says, "WHAT?" Sabrina starts walking towards the driveway, Marshall trying to stop her and says, "What happened?" Sabrina keeps walking and doesn't look his way while saying, "Marshall, do you even love me?" Marshall, with his voice cracking, replies, "Of course!" Sabrina stops and looks Marshall in the eyes. "Marshall, do you really love me more than you love your dream?" Marshall being as sympathetic as anyone could be, replied in a low tone, "I want

you to be part of my dream." Sabrina starts to steam, "No! Marshall, do you love me more than your dream?"

Marshall doesn't answer, then he drops to his knees and hugs her waist, but Sabrina being fed up, pulls his arms from around her waist and walks into the cab. You hear the children crying as the cab pulls off. Marshall watches as the cab pulls off the shattered shell of Marshall, then sits on the curb holding his head.

OUTSIDE OF THE ISLEY BROTHERS STUDIO - NIGHT

Four songs into the Album Observation in Time Pee Wee, Marshall and Joe are outside in the alley drinking some liquor and smoking a joint. Marshall passes the Joint to Joe. Joe inhales the Joint, then exhales and says, "Pee Wee, why you always holding the bottle so long? Pass it over, man." Pee Wee drunk points his finger on Joe's chest, then gets right up as far as he can get in Joe's face, then says, "Look motherfucker! I'm the alcoholic in this band! We ain't put in for an alcoholic slash singer." Joe doesn't pay the dunking Pee Wee no mind; then he turns to Marshall, saying, "Say, Marshall, we all split the writing and performing credits, right?" Marshall exhales the smoke and then looks at Joe with a stinking look "Yeah? Why? You've been asking me that all day?" Joe tries to play it cool "No reason, but even if…" Marshall interrupts Joe, pissed off, then looks in his face and says,

"But even if nothing!" Pee Wee drunk points and laughs at Joe, then Marshall joins in. Joe laughs along but turns with a wicked look on his face.

The very next day, Joe is a no-show at the studio.
So Marshall, tired of being tired, try to handle
things before Greg and Satch show up. Marshall
gets Producer Johnny Brantley to call Joe while
Marshall stands next to him looking upset. Johnny
gets Joe on the phone. "Joe, you coming?
Everybody's here?" Joe's speaking so loud even
Marshall can hear him through the phone. "I can't
work with those assholes! Mail my check, man."
You hear the phone hang up. Johnny shakes his
head no to Marshall. Marshall slams his hand on the
table and says, "What the fuck, again! Every time
we go one step forward, something pushes us back!
We recorded some good fuckin records with Joe
too. Capital ain't gonna like this shit at all." Johnny
replies, "To hell with that; we're keeping those
recordings!" Pee Wee jumps off the couch and
walks in front of everyone with his hands up,
gesturing to hold on. "Hold on y'all, wait one
minute. I got an idea." Twenty minutes later, Pee
Wee brings in Dutch Robinson, 6 foot 2 inches,
medium build, with the voice like an angel. Pee
Wee points to Dutch. "This is Dutch Robinson; we
already went over the song! And boy, is he ready!"
Greg being there for a few minutes is

hip to what's going on. He walks over to Pee Wee
and whispers in his ear while looking at Dutch,
"You sure about this?

Pee Wee puts his hand up to gesture to wait a minute to Greg; then, he gestures to Dutch to go to the mic. As everyone takes their places in the studio. Johnny standing next to the studio engineer talks to everyone through the crosstalk. "OK, take it from the top then." The band plays the instrumental to "Over the Rainbow" by the Ohio Players. As soon as Dutch starts to sing his first high note, you see the needles on the dial jump to the top. The engineer points to the needle to show Johnny, Johnny never seeing this, yells "WHOA STOP!!!" Everyone stops playing, and Johnny thrilled says through the crosstalk, "Dutch, what the fuck! Wow, I have never seen that before! We can't record those high notes you're hitting. Man! You got a set of pipes on you. Dutch, you're gonna have to come down one octave. This equipment can't handle it." The band members look at each other in amazement after hearing what Johnny said. Dutch puts his hands up, gesturing, I don't know.

SATCH'S HOUSE - NIGHT

At a party for the completion of the album "Observation in Time" at Satch's house. Full of black sexy female and male friends with a lot of drinking going on. Some sit on the living room floor smoking weed in the low-lit room, talking.

A white record promoter next to Satch tries to pass the joint to the black guy sitting next to him with dark shades on, but he's too high; he waves his hands, gesturing he'll pass. Then he passes it back to Satch. Satch inhales the smoke and exhales. Then Satch walks over to the White female dressed in a sexy hippie, gets up and gives her a shotgun (blowing smoke into her mouth.) The female hippie exhales the smoke, then gets her boogie on. Satch sits back down, and a fine black female hugs him from behind. Satch's wife Carolyn, walking out the kitchen, stops seeing Satch hugged up. Carolyn looks at Satch with a look that could kill.

Carolyn starts to march towards Satch hellbent, but her sister seeing this, runs over and grabs her arm, pulling her back while saying, "Girl, just let him be! Trust if I thought it was something we'd already been on her ass." Carolyn smiles, and they get ready to walk off, and Carolyn looks back, and Satch stands up then grabs the sexy black girl from behind him and, holding her hand up in the air, says, "Hey y'all look here! Her Mama used to beat me & her older brother's asses to get the music right. When you go home, kiss my auntie and tell her I love her.

Satch kisses her on the forehead and winks at Carolyn. Carolyn's sister looks at her and says, "See, I told you! Baby sis, my whoop-ass detector ain't never been wrong!

Now come on, the boy slick, but he ain't stupid. Carolyn looks back, and her sister pulls her arm to come on. Dutch is in the kitchen talking a whole lot of nothing to anybody that walks in the room. Marshall walks in the kitchen, and Dutch's eyes light up, Dutch being as loud as anyone could be. "Marshall!!! I got this young keyboard player from right here in Dayton." Marshall tries to ignore him, knowing Satch sent him in the kitchen to sober up. Marshall reaches and grabs a beer from the cooler beside Dutch. Marshall opens the beer with his key and replies, "Yeah?" Dutch seeing, he has Marshall's attention, shoots his shot. "Man, you gonna love him. His name is Junie." Marshall pauses, looking at how drunk Dutch is. "Junie?" Dutch barely stands up and says, "Walter Morrison, but they call him Junie. We can meet him at the school tomorrow." Marshall looks up at Dutch with a confused look on his face. "School? Man, we don't want no babies?" Dutch starts to laugh loudly.

ROOSEVELT HIGH SCHOOL, FIELD - DAY - SUMMER 1970

The next day Dutch and Marshall show up at Roosevelt High School to meet a 17yr old, Walter Junie Morrison, a short dark skin teenager with a whole lot of style. Junie's standing with his keyboard, talking to two chicks. Dutch nudges

Marshall with his elbow to show him Junie across the street, and they walk over to him. Dutch introduces them, "Junie!!! What's happening, young brother? This here's Marshall, our bass player I told you about."

Junie hit Marshall with a hip new handshake. Marshall, confused, does it with Junie. Junie, "Hey Marshall, what's shakin'?" Marshall replies, "I hear you real good on that?" Junie, trying to impress the girls, smirks at them and says, "I'll let the keyboard answer that!" Junie, Marshall, Dutch and the girls walk over to the bleachers, and Junie plugs in his keyboard. Marshall, standing facing Junie, says, "OK! Let's see what you got!" Junie starts to play, and it sounds good. Marshall plays it cool. "That's cool; now play something more musical?" Junie plays it easy and amazes the two girls standing next to him. Marshall really tries to challenge Junie. "How bout something funky?" Junie smiles at Marshall then plays it with a cutting-edge twist. Marshall looks at Junie with a silly grin saying, "I like you, man! I like you. How old are you? Cause we can't take babies on the road." Junie, sticking his chest out to impress the two girls he's with, replies, "Baby! Man, I'm seventeen!" Marshall looks at Junie pauses, trying to see if he could rattle him, but Junie puts his lip up, gesturing to stop lying. Then Marshall says, "Get your bags ready!"

Then one of the two girls hugs Junie as they celebrate.

COMPASS RECORDS OFFICE - AFTERNOON - 1969

At this time, the Ohio Players are back and forth between Dayton, Ohio and New York City. The band walks into the Compass' A&R Department to go over their project.

Greeting them at the door is a young white woman as they walk in looking very happy and excited. The band is escorted to the A&R of the project. The A&R points to six seats with a smile and says, "Fellas, have a seat." Everyone takes a seat, smiling. The A&R says, "Now I told you guys I'll go to bat for guys, right?" Greg smiling says, "Right!" The A&R looks Greg right in the eyes. "Well, they're not pitching the ball to me anymore!" Satch, confused, looks at Greg. The A&R seeing that Satch is confused answers his concerns, "Satch, what they said you're just not commercial enough! It's just not selling!" Greg looks at Dutch mad. Satch gets what he's saying then starts shaking his head. Greg puts his hand up, gesturing to wait a minute, "We got new material; you really gonna like this." Marshall stands up facing the A&R behind the desk and says, "Before you say what you're about to say, I think you're going to regret it! We want this more than we want our next breath! This bass has taken me across this country twice! Now it's time to see the world!"

Everyone looks at Marshall, shocked., then the A&R says, "It's not my decision; I put my career on the line for you guys. Sorry but we gotta let you guys go." Satch and Sugarfoot are the first to storm out of the office, followed by everyone except Marshall,

who turns around at the door then points his finger at the A&R and says, "Remember what I told..." Greg grabs Marshall from behind, interrupting him pulling him out the door.

DRESSING ROOM OAK LEAF NIGHT CLUB DAYTON, OHIO - NIGHT

The Band at this time is picking up minor gigs to get by. Everyone is in the dressing room except Dutch. After having the Band miss getting paid for the second time in a month, and the Band is in the dressing room mad as hell. Marshall, in disbelief, says, "I can't believe Dutch with this not showing up shit again. And I just left him!" Junie jumps off the couch to show Marshall a newspaper article wanting to kill the negative vibe. "Man, whatever!

Marshall, I'm gonna turn you on to the 1969 National Black Economic Development Conference and the creation of the Black Manifesto."

One weekend in late April 1969, more than 500 Black activists, organizers, clergy, and businesspeople will gather in Detroit, Michigan, for a conference with the aim of discussing Black people's economic situations in the U.S. and strategies for our community development.

Bursting through the door is Dutch showing up drunk and high on something with a girl under his arm, making a grand entrance. "And this is the Ohio Players!" Marshall pushes Junie from in front of him and goes over to Dutch. "Dutch, you gotta show up to be in da band.

You missed the show again; look at you!" Greg, pissed off, stands beside Marshall and says, "Again with this shit Dutch?"

Dutch, swaying back and forth, puts his arms up for a hug. Greg stops him by putting his hand out then looks him up and down with disgust. Dutch being disgustingly unsympathetic, says, "C'mon baby, these motherfuckers are bringing me down right now." Greg normally would go for the routine, but after the missed shows, he's had it, and without any hesitation, he points to the door and says, "Dutch, we not doing this shit again; you out!" Dutch, drunk and just not giving a fuck puts his hand gesturing he doesn't give a fuck, as he thinks the band needs him. Then Dutch leaves with the two ladies he walked in with, with his head up high. Greg shaking his head says, I'm glad Satch ain't here. He would have whooped the boys butt again. Then Greg shaking his head walks back out the room.

CHAPTER TEN

SATCH HOUSE - DUSK - WINTER 1970

A few weeks later, the band is in Satch's living room, packed and ready to hit the road. Greg thinks Pee Wee must be in the van as he's been asking everyone in the house for Pee Wee. Greg seeing Satch walking in the front door back from the van, says, "Satch, where's Pee Wee? His bag's right here."

Satch walks in the front door looking real cold. "He's not in the van; I just put my bags in there." Marshall stands up and says, "Pee Wee was talkin' about quitting the band again, but I thought he was just bitchin'." Greg makes everyone spread out to look for Pee Wee. About fifteen minutes into looking, Sugarfoot being a little worried, grabs Marshall by the shoulder and says, "Marshall... Pee Wee's OK, man." Marshall replies, "Yeah, he's just fed up with all the singers we keep finding, and they all end up doing us wrong."

Junie, hearing Marshall looks down and away without saying a word. Everyone can be seen looking around, and nobody can find Pee Wee, and one by one, all of them hit the couch, giving up the search except Marshall. Marshall finally finds him hiding in the basement, curled up with a bottle of wine. Marshall approaches him real slow, "Hey, man, you OK?" Pee Wee, crying and upset, puts down the wine, then wipes his eyes sobbing says, "I'm tired, man! Every time we get a new singer, the same shit happens. I thought we finally had something with Dutch. Now fuckin' Capital dropped us! Marshall, I can't do this no more." Marshall bends down to catch eye contact with Pee Wee. In a very consoling tone, Marshall says, "It's not your fault, Pee Wee! We've been through a lot, eleven years, man! we'll get through this together!" Pee Wee smirks, then replies, "Damn, man, everybody else gave up. I heard 'em. But not you, man." Marshall, feeling the love, smiles, too. "Pee Wee, we go back a long way, you, me and Satch." Marshall helped his friend up. Marshall walks off in front of Pee Wee, and Pee Wee calls him, "Hey Marshall."

Marshall stops, then turns around said "Yeah?" Pee Wee walks up and hugs his friend and says, "Thanks, man."

BUFFALO NY BUS STATION - NIGHT

Marshall and Greg, sitting in their van and a Greyhound Bus in Buffalo, NY. The bus pulls up, and four people get off, and Charles Dale Allen is standing looking around as everyone else is being greeted by friends or loved ones. Greg smiles and taps Marshall, and they get out of the van. Greg says, "Dale?" Greg looks at Marshall and whispers, "He looks just like Johnny said." Marshall being sarcastic, replies in a low tone, "Nuts... but he can sing, and we got gigs, right?" Greg looking unsure, says, "Man, whatever." Greg stretch's his hand out, and Dale smiles in a corky way and shakes his and Marshall's hand. Dale, with his hand, stretched out, introduces himself, "Charles Dale Allen, but everybody calls me Dale." Dale stands there with a goofy look on his face, smiling and looking goofy.

Two months after the band hits the stage performing their first take of "Proud Mary" by The Ohio Players. Dale, at the lead, steps to the front of the stage, pointing to the audience, acting as if he's on the phone. Junie makes a phone ringing sound, and Dale says, "Man, I hope granny doesn't answer. Hello?" In the silly voice Junie uses on "Funky Worm," Junie acts as if he's a granny saying, "What you calling for, she don't want you no more."

Dale being silly, holding his hand by his ear like a phone, says, "GRANNY, put her on the phone!" The audience goes crazy, and Dale looks back to a smiling Junie and Junie playing Granny says, "Boy,

111

she don't want your crusty ass. Stop calling
disturbing me with your old, tired-sounding ass...
Bye." Dale hits the floor and acts as if he's crushed,
then goes back into the song as the audience
screams for Dale and the band.

BUFFALO TOWNHOUSE - DAY

Marshall and Sugarfoot playing chess, and Marshall
makes a move, and he points to the Chess Board,
and he says, "Checkmate!" Sugarfoot starts to look,
and Marshall says, "What? What you gonna do?"
Sugarfoot, not really paying attention, says, "Ok, I
see it... Marshall, let me ask you something?"
Marshall packing the chessboard up, stops in
concern, then he sits down and says, "Shoot."
Sugarfoot looks around then says, "Man, thirteen
years, and I still haven't gone home to see mama
yet. You think she would be upset wit me?"
Marshall smiles then says, "One thing I can say is
you have a strong, stubborn will, just like me. Boy,
you're hardheaded." Sugarfoot smiles, sitting across
from Marshall, looking at him with empathy, and
the door slams. Junie and Dale are going at it. Dale,
with his fingers in Junie's face, says, "Marshall,
Foots, how you work with this kid?" Junie looks at
Marshall pathetically, and Marshall jumps up to
Junie's defense. "What happened?"

"This Meatball just fucked up some fine, and I do mean fine coochie, this guy." Marshall waves his hand and sits back down. Sugarfoot smiles and Greg and Pee Wee walk in through the door. Greg has a couple of bags in his hand. Greg places one of the bags on the table in front of Marshall and Sugarfoot.

Marshall looks in the bag, saying, "Soap, toothpaste and deodorant. What's this for?" Greg, with a wicked grin, says, "Another thirty-One-Niter's we leave at midnight." Greg walks off, and Sugarfoot smiles at Marshall, who starts to shake his head.

ON-STAGE, COTTON CLUB - NIGHT

The band is at the world-famous Cotton Club, and Dale is on-stage dancing, doing the skate like he was James Brown and the crowd cheers. Dale points to the band, and the band starts to play the song "Here Today Gone Tomorrow" by the Ohio Players. As the song ends Junie looks at Dale, and Dale yells, "NOW Y'ALL READY FOR SOMETHING HOT!" The audience replies, "yeah." Then Dale points to Junie and says, "Sometimes a man feels like trespassing on somebody else's property." The band starts to play the instrumental to "Trespassin'," by the Ohio Players. The crowd starts to go wild. Dale points

to Greg then you see Greg beating a mean drum
solo with an intense look on his face. The crowd
dances to the drum, and Satch and Pee Wee steps
to the front laying, heavy horns parts to the drums.
Then the rest of the band comes back in with Dale
on the lead singing his heart out. The crowd goes
wild, and you see two girls in the front row point
to Dale and Satch, then back to themselves. Satch
looks at Dale and nods his head. Then, Dale gives
the girls the thumbs up.

BACKSTAGE COTTON CLUB - NIGHT

Marshall is sitting in a corner by himself
with his head down, and Greg walks over to
him and says, "What's wrong with you,
Marshall? You never stick around to help
me pack the equipment away. Right now,
you and Pee Wee would be off doing
something crazy; what's up?" Marshall
picks his head up, and with a look of rage,
he blurts out. "What the fuck we really
doing?! This is chump change!" Walking
into the room, Dale and a sexy fine sister
with an afro and a super short mini skirt can
be seen. He stops at the door, and Greg
gestures for him to wait. Dale and his lady
for the night walk out of the room but then
duck off to the side to listen to Greg and

Marshall. Greg playing big brother, says, "Marshall, what happened?" Marshall looks Greg square in the eyes, and Greg looks shocked, never seeing Marshall come at him like this. Marshall, way up in his feeling, says, "We've been doing this same song and dance for years. Don't get me wrong; the show money is not bad; eighty-five dollars a night is good but, we need to make it to the next level. Now the label's saying Dale is not going to work."

What we gonna do now?" The lady standing with Dale lets go of his arm. Greg trying to reel Marshall back in, says, "Now hold on, Marshall, we stay getting compared to the Jazz Crusaders over and over again. We cut three records with Dale, but nothing so far caught any labels attention." The lady standing with Dale in the hallway walks away, and Dale quietly gestures for her to wait, but she waves him off (as to say get lost.) Marshall's face gets serious again, then he stands up and looks Greg straight in the eyes, saying. "Look, I like to have fun with the ladies, but I like the money more; fix it!" Then Marshall walks out.

The next week the band is in the booth recording singing in the morning by the Ohio Players. Junnie is on the keyboard, talking into the mic in his grannie's voice. "The Ohio Players, Singing In the Morning... Did I say It right?" Dale replies, "Yeah." Junie says, "Good, now pay me my money!" Dale starts to sing his heart out, and Satch looks at Greg and Marshall, shaking his head in denial. Satch and Pee Wee lay some heavy horn parts. Then Junnie comes with some heavy keyboard playing, and they jam out to Dale harmonizing to the track. Then Junnie changes the groove, making it smooth and Jazzy to close it out. The room gets quiet; Satch looks up at the recording light on the wall, and as it goes off, so does Satch.

Satch runs up in the face of Dale like he's about to take his head off and yells, "WHAT THE FUCK WAS THAT?" Dale, cocky and confident, says, "That shit was a hit! What the fuck you talking about?" Marshall and Pee Wee both rush to grab Satch, who's about to punch Dale. Greg rushes over to protect Dale and Marshall, holding Satch back, says, "Satch, chill out, man." Satch angrily says, "CHILL OUT! Ok, I'm cool... Marshall, chill out, I'm cool!" Marshall and Pee Wee both reluctantly let him go, and Satch and he fixes his shirt. Satch acts like he's cool, then he pushes Marshall out the way and heads for Dale. Greg standing in front of Dale, yells at the charging Satch, "DON'T HIT ME!!! CHILL OUT, SATCH!" Satch, pissed, says, "Get the fuck out the way, and I won't." Dale, completely frustrated with the whole situation, puts his head down and his hands up, as to say I give up, and he says, "I may not have the best voice, but I come and give it my all." Satch seeing him cower, tones his bravado down and says, "Look, no offense, but we've been at this since forever! What you doing as a performer is amazing, but we need a hit record, like yesterday. Your voice is not doing it for the labels." Marshall Jumps in between them and says, "How about this you stick around, stay on the road wit us. This way, we can both grease our pockets until you find you a situation, or we do, cool?"

Dale being nonchalant, says, "Man, whatever." Dale turns around and mumbles under his breath, "Not like you motherfuckers gon' do shit, anyway." Satch, hearing this, loses it, charging after Dale. Greg points at Dale and says, "Just go... I heard that bullshit." Johnnie walks into the booth, and Dale stops, thinking Johnny's going to save him and Johnny, already hearing everything through the crosstalk, says, "Get the fuck outta here! Nobody wants that shit around them!" Dale walks off, and a special unity and camaraderie between the band and producer begin.

REHEARSAL STUDIO NEW YORK - DAY - SUMMER 1971

The band is playing the instrumental to "Singing In The Morning" by the Ohio Players. Greg puts his hands up, gesturing to stop, and he says, "Whoa, hold on... we need a singer, bad." Pee Wee, in his groove, stops, then looks at Greg, frustrated about hearing this, and he says, "Who we gonna get?" Marshall takes off his strap on his bass and puts it down; then he looks at Greg as if he's tired of hearing it, and to Pee Wee's defense as always, Marshall jumps right in, saying, "I'm tired of singers taking advantage of us, not to mention all the bullshit they bring! Dale's starting this, not showing up shit already?" Junie jumps up off the couch, looking serious, and says, "Hey, I can sing!" Everyone in the band starts to say no, hell no, and any other no they could find to Junie.

Junie, still trying, says, "What...? I can, too, sing!" Greg gets in between Junie and the band and says, "OK, hold on, Junie, let's see what you got." The band began to play "My Girl" by The Temptations, and Junie stopped them, saying, "Naw man, hold on! Play that new song by Eddie Kendricks." The band plays "All By Myself" by Eddie Kendricks. Junie begins to sing; not before long, Pee Wee starts playing slurred notes then stopping. Pee Wee, hearing enough, says, "Man, I thought you said you

118

could sing?" Junie, with a crackle in his voice, says, "I can sing." Pee Wee shaking his head, replies, "If you call that singing, we in trouble." The band starts to laugh, and Junie puts his head down, and a tear falls, and Pee Wee really lets him have it. Greg, feeling bad for Junie, walks in front of Pee Wee and everyone in the band with his arms out, and he says, "Now hold on, Pee Wee... Junie, I think with a little work, you might have something, now don't fuck this up."

The band makes it back to New York without a lead singer. Being as talented as they were, being a musician was still good work. While inside a recording studio, the band starts to play the instrumental to "Pain" by the Ohio Players. Greg getting excited, yells, "KEEP THAT GROOVE!" The band continues to play, then all of a sudden, Greg waves his hand to get everyone's attention. "Hold on; we gotta record this!

After all these years, this will be our first original record!" Marshall says, "You said you don't trust them." Greg excitedly walks out of the room towards the engineer but holds his leg in pain as he walks off. Greg goes in the booth and gives the engineer a few dollars to record the record, then walks back over to the band. Greg gets everyone in their places in the booth holding their instruments, and Marshall winks at Junie. Junie puts his thumb up, then Greg on the drums slapping his sticks together; the band starts to play the instrumental to "Pain" by the Ohio Players. Junie starts to sing from way down deep in his heart, "PAIN, IS IN MY HEART!"

A week later, Greg is in the radio station getting interviewed by a hip young black disc Jockey with a heavy NY accent. Pain by the Ohio Players plays in the background. Greg was happy to hear the record. The disc jockey turns the mic and says, "Ok, we'll be back with our segment of Rising Stars with Greg Webster of "The Ohio Players." Then the Disc Jockey turns to Greg and says, "I took this record to my boss, and he said the same thing I did. Man, it's a hit!" Greg replied, "YEAH?" The disc jockey seeing Greg, really doesn't get what he's saying, explains, "But like I told you, we can't do shit with it till it's cleared.

You got a monster on your hands; get it cleared!" Greg goes to say something, but the Disc Jockey puts his hand up, gesturing wait, cutting Greg off. Then the disc jockey reaches over to a big phone interface with flashing lights and presses one of the light phone lines flashing. The disc jockey leans over, talking into the Mic in a totally different voice. "Caller?" The caller #1 voice is a hip-sounding Brooklyn accent, and it comes through the speakers saying, "Aye, this is Tony from

BROOKLYN! Did you say the Ohio Players, Pain?" The Disc Jockey points to Greg and smiles saying, "That's right, Tony. What do you have to say about that track?" Caller #1 says, "That's was some of the Funkiest shi... Excuse me, but you's got something going on... I wanna hear more." The disc jockey presses the button on the lit phone interface and says, "HELLO, WELCOME TO THE HOTTEST SHOW IN THE MORNING; what's on your mind, caller?" Caller #2 A real righteous sister with a New York accent says, "You said Ohio Players, my brother?" The disc jockey replies, "Yeah, that's right!" Caller #2, being fully animated, says, "Loving this vibe y'all Keep it up!"

The Disc Jockey moves from the mic, then turns to Greg, pointing to the switchboard lighting up, and says, "Look, man, all these lines are for your track. Get that release now; you got a hit in New York City, come on?" Greg sat there smiling on the outside while burning on the inside.

The very next morning, Greg jumps right on the phone demanding answers while Satch stands next to him, looking angry. Off to the side, Marshall, Pee Wee, Sugarfoot, and Junie are seen looking concerned. Greg slams the phone to hang it up. Right away, Greg picks it right back up and dials a number. Then he turns to Satch, mad as hell, and says, "Those motherfuckers out of Akron trying to fuck us!" Greg dials a number, and someone answers, "That's why I'm calling the manufacturing plant... hello!" Greg stays on the phone for a few minutes, walking back and forth, stretching the cord, then Greg slams the phone, and Satch turns to look at Greg. Greg angrily yells, "THESE MOTHERFUCKERS!!!" Satch tries to ask what happened, but Greg pissed off, shuts him down, then Greg picks the phone up and dials another number steaming. Someone answers, and Greg speaking louder than anyone in the band ever heard him talk, yells, "LOOK, CUT THE BULLSHIT! I called the manufacturing plant, and they said y'all didn't pay for shit!

Greg pauses to listen as Satch stands next to him, looking pissed. Greg, still stretching the cord, yells, "WHO THE FUCK YOU PLAYING WITH! Listen, either you pay, or we take the album and shop it ourselves!" Greg yells as he walks right by Junie, causing Junie to stand straight up from being dead asleep on the couch. Then Greg pauses to listen to the response, and his face gets even more irate.

Greg, not getting anywhere, looks at Satch, then he gives his ultimatum, "FUCK YOU! You got a week, put up or shut up!" Greg slams the phone, and Satch puts his hand up, gesturing what happened. Greg sits on the chair in the kitchen and says, "That why Pain was the only original on the whole album. Tell you what, we gonna find us another situation." Satch replies, "Capitol should have waited, damn man." Later that week, working the record "Pain" in a nightclub in New York, Greg packing his drums on-stage is approached by Herb James and Billy Pittman looking like sharks seeing blood. Billy starts talking loudly to Greg over the music, "Excuse me! Hey! Can I talk to you?" Greg yells over the music, "What's happenin'?"

Billy extends his hand and says, "Hi, I'm Billy Pittman, and this is my partner Herb James, and we're from Westbound Records." Greg, not really feeling them, doesn't smile. "What can I do for you?" Billy still yelling over the music, "Is there somewhere we can go? I'd like to speak with the band." Greg replies, "Yeah, OK, follow me." Billy and Herb turned around, shocked, as they didn't expect the whole band to be standing right behind them. Greg gestures to follow him. Marshall walks ahead next to Greg on the way in the room and says, "Are we in some kinda trouble?" Greg replies, "Nah, these jokers came up to me and said they were from Westbound. We do need a new label after Capital dropped us."

Marshall shrugs his shoulders. "Yeah, but these motherfuckers look shaky, man." Greg nods his head, and they both look in the room at Billy and

Herb smiling and shaking hands with the band looking shaky. Greg and Marshall enter the dressing room with everyone in the dressing room, and Billy introduces himself, "My name is Billy Pittman, and this is Herb James. We just signed a group named 'Funkadelics,' and we really think you guys fit the direction we're going at Westbound Records." Herb walks over to Junie and puts his hand on Junie's shoulder. "You can all go to the studio, where you guys will record and not have to pay for it." Marshall puts his hand up, gesturing to stop, "Hold the fuck on!"

Satch catching the vibe, jumps in front of Marshall, looking angry, "What the fuck you tryna lay on us, man?" Billy puts his hand up, gesturing no problem to Satch, then says, "All I'm saying is, you record, and we pay for the distribution and all recordings." Junie's eyes light up, catching everybody's attention. Billy walks over to Junie with a wicked smile and says, "Even Royalties." Greg walks in front of Junie and says, "Sounds good coming out your mouth! but it would sound much better in writing, ya dig!" Billy puts his hand up as if no offense. Billy says, "Here's my number, and we'll talk about all the terms to close this deal." Greg takes the card and, looking Billy straight in the eyes, says, "OK, but this ain't our first rodeo." Billy and Herb smile at each other, and they shake Greg's hand then leave the room. Marshall, Greg, and Pee Wee look at each other as if they don't trust them, while Junie looks at Herb and Billy walking out, and he puts his hand on his chin, wondering. The next week, the band arrives at Westbound records to re-record the record "Pain." The Ohio Players are in the Lobby, and Greg looks over to Junie sitting on the couch with his feet up, in a nice pair of dark shades, looking like a superstar. Greg nervous as it was all on, Junie says, "Don't fuck this up! We got everything's ride on this!"

Junie being a cocky little kid, tries to brush Greg off. "Man, I got you!" Satch knowing Greg taps him on his shoulder to calm him down. Greg catching the drift, changes his vibe "Satch, remember that crazy horn part I told you about?" Satch nodded his head and put his thumb up while looking at Junie with a serious look. Junie seeing Satch avoids eye contact. Then Greg looks over to Marshall, "Marshall, bring it heavy! Pee Wee, this track's got a lot of accents on the horn parts; lay it on em thick!" Greg looks in Junie's direction while pointing. Marshall waves his hand, gesturing to leave him alone. Everyone walks out, giving Junie some stink looks, except Marshall. Marshall stops Junie on the way out the door as he sees Junie looking stressed and broken and says, "Remember, perform the record like there's an audience in front of you, and you're singing to the sexiest girl in the front row." Junie smiles then nod his head in approval. Marshall and Junie leave the room. After the recording, everyone in the band felt satisfied. Junie is in the Hallway talking to Apple, an eighteen-year-old, very sassy and sexy light-skinned young lady looking as if she doesn't want to be bothered with him. Herb is seen walking in a hurry to the studio seeing Junie, he stops looking very enthusiastic and eager, and he says, "JUNIE, YOU DID IT! We just took your record 'Pain' upstairs, and they approved it! Not only did they approve it, but they put it as a priority. Junie, you're gonna be a star!"

Herb walks off fast back into the studio, and Junie turns back to Apple, who is standing in front of Junie with a new attitude. "OK, superstar, where you taking me?" Junie smiles, then puts his hand out, gesturing to hold on. "Oh, is that right? Two minutes ago, you told me you was here to meet a real star. Not somebody trying to make it!" Apple looks Junie up and down, "Boy, my mama told me, destiny is to be in the right place at the right time! AND BOY, YOU AIN'T GOING NOWHERE!" Junie grabs Apple's hand, and they walk into the studio to cheers for Junie.

The next week Marshall, Satch, and Greg sit down to meet Herb, Billy, and Joel Brodsky, who's sitting there with a briefcase on the floor by his foot.

Joel Brodsky is a white Brooklyn, NY native with a heavy Brooklyn accent. Everyone shakes hands, and Herb says, "Fellas! Joel Brodsky is the hottest photographer in the business. Joel, let's see what you came up with?" Joel reaches for his briefcase by his foot and places it on his lap, and says, "Greg, when we spoke, you said you want a female on the cover, right?" Greg replies, "Right." Then Joel looks at Marshall, saying, "Marshall, you said you guys have a different sense of style, right?" Marshall nods his head in approval, then Joel looks at Satch with a silly grin then starts nodding his head. Joel seeing Satch puts a big smile on his face, then being as animated as he could be, saying, "SATCH... Now you gave me the idea and the vision when we spoke." Satch pops his collar and says, "Yeah, you know." Joel points his finger at Satch. "You said to make it sexual, make it stand out, and don't hold back! So here it is." Joel turns the picture around, and everyone's eyes light up. Marshall, Greg, and Satch start to slap fives. The pain cover has bald-headed model Pat Running Bear Evans on the cover. Marshall Greg and Stach riding by a record shop, sees the record in three different teenagers' hands walking out the record shops excited. Satch opens a Newspaper and shows everyone the "Pain" reached thirty-five on the US R&B Chart and Twenty-one on the U.S Billboard top soul LP's.

As they drive up to Westbound Records parking lot, they see Junie and Apple wearing matching white mink coats while walking a little white poodle as fans swarm him for autographs. At this point, the Ohio Players considering the time, set a tone for the seventies with Pat Evans dominating a man on the Pain's Album Cover. The album cover touches cultural, social, and all the same racially driven political issues we share even today.

SOUL TRAIN TV STUDIO - DAY - WINTER 1972

The band in Soultrain TV Studio, standing backstage, sees Gladys Knight and the Pips walk off the stage from a standing ovation. Greg gives everyone in the band the don't fuck up look, then reinforced by Satch. One of the TV producers walks over, calling them to the stage. On the way on the stage, Marshall stops Pee Wee saying, "You believe this, national TV, Don Cornelius and those sexy Soultrain Dancers, MAN!" Pee Wee smiles, seeing how excited Marshall is, then Don Cornelius introduces the band to the stage with Junie at the lead. Don Cornelius holding a long skinny microphone standing center stage, says, "The album Pain has fueled these brothers to respond with their follow up smash hit 'Pleasure.' Using the oh-so-sexy model Pat 'Running Bear'' Evans on their cover again. These brothers have made it! Let's give it up for 'The Ohio Players.'" The band Ohio Players walks on stage performing, 'Pain' rocking the stage, and all you see is Afro's bobbing to the music. After the performance, Don Cornelius enters the stage and approaches Satch, saying, "You guys are super funky, all of yall! I guess you think I'm stupid for asking if you are all really from Ohio?" Then Don puts the mic over to Satch's mouth.

Satch, chuckling, says, "Yeah, man, we all from Ohio." Don asks another interview question, "Why do y'all call yourselves players?" Don puts the mic over Satch's mouth. "We like the word 'players' to pertain to music, and a player has to have soul, rock and jazz, all of it." The cameraman zooms in close on Don Cornelius, and he says, "And there you have it! Look for great things to come and give it up one more time for the Ohio Players!"

BAR IN NEW YORK CITY - NIGHT

The band is back in New York, and Marshall, Junie, and Satch walk into the bar. They stop looking towards the booths to see a sharply dressed, muscular-built black man calling them over. Junie walks in front, waving as if it's his friend as they walk over. Off to the side, two black men can be seen sitting across from them, and one of them has a camera under the table taking pictures. While the other black man at the table shakes his head and smiles. Junie approaches the sharply dressed, muscular black man with his arms stretched out, and they hug as if they are good friends. The black man who is sitting across starts to snap more pictures of Junie and the sharply dressed man. Junie turns to Marshall, and Satch then says, "This here's Marshall, our bass player, and Satch, the real official player of the group. Y'all meet my main man, Frank Lucas." Frank smiles, saying, "Junie, you crazy man. Y'all sit down, have a drink on me."

Frank calls over the waitress, a foxy black young lady, "Betty, do me a favor, run me over two glasses of that yack you just brought me." Betty sees Satch, and they lock eyes. Then Betty gives Satch a seductive look then walks off. Satch seeing her walk away swinging her ass points to Betty and looks at Frank, and he shrugs his shoulders (As if to say go ahead.) Satch says, "Good looking, my brother. I'll be right back." Satch gets up, then walks over and puts his arm around the smiling Betty, and the men at the table take more pictures.

Frank looking at Satch, says, "He's a real smooth motherfucker, I give him that. Junie, you wanted some smoke, right?" Junie replied, "Yeah, two ounces." Frank calls over a black tough-looking young man, and he says, "Go give them two ounces of that iky sticky."

The black tough-looking young man takes his backpack off and goes in it, and grabs two ounces of weed. He tries to hand it to Frank, but Frank looks at him like he's crazy. The tough-looking young man catches what's going on and passes it to Junie, who stretches his hand out. The men at the table across start to take more pictures, and the other black man shakes his head in approval and gets up and walks off. Satch returns with Betty, who serves Marshall and Junie their drinks. Satch, with his drink in his hand, raises it and says, "TO SUCCESS!!!"

They all raise their glasses to toast while the pictures keep snapping. Junie passes Marshall the weed under the table, and Marshall says, "This shit smells good; how much I got for you?" Frank replies, "Man, we good! Junie's da my man, but I gotta split. Next rounds on me. Junie, don't be a stranger." Frank leaves some money on the table, then gets up to leave, and Junie gives him a five, and they bump shoulders of respect as they part while the pictures snap.

Junie, Satch, and Marshall walk out of the club laughing, and Marshall turns to both of them and says, "I gotta piss; I'll meet y'all." Satch waves his hand to go ahead. Then Junie and Satch walk outside the doors to a gun's barrel pointing at Junie's and a voice yelling, "MOVE, I FUCKIN DARE YOU'S!" The White Detective in his mid 30's, with a heavy native New Yorkers accent, pushes Junie to the wall while the other three White Detectives surround Satch. Then the officers cuff Satch and take him into a paddy wagon. The White Detective slams Junie's face up against the wall, then goes into Junie's pocket and whips out a wad of cash and says, "I fucking hate to see you niggas walking around with more money than me! This is my country, boy!" Junie, just as cocky as could be, said, "Whatever! My lawyer is going to treat your white ass the same way." The Detective punches Junie in his side, then grabs Junie's arm behind his back and chicken wings him from the wall to the cop car, slamming him on the car.

Just then, an old cop with Sergeant stripes on his uniform is seen driving by real slow as the car rides by; the Sergeant tips his hat to the Detective holding Junie in the car. He nods back to the Sergeant, then cuffs Junie and puts him in the car. Then the two unmarked cop cars drive off. Marshall walks out the door to see there's no one standing there as he looks towards the corner. Marshall sees the unmarked cop car stop at the corner. All of a sudden, he sees Satch getting thrown from the unmarked cop car, and he rolls on the concrete. The two unmarked cop cars drive off while Marshall runs down the block to Satch. Satch, scraped up and in pain, sits on the curb then says, "They took Junie, Somethin' 'bout being a drug dealer." Marshall smiling, says, "That boy's broke, come on, I got this weed on me, plus everybody already left for Dayton, come on!"

Marshall helps Satch up, and the two walk off. Satch starts to limp while grunting in pain; then, he stops to reach into his sock and pulls out a bag of cocaine to take a long hit. Satch offers it to Marshall, but he gestures no then says, "How long you been fucking around wit that shit, Satch?" Satch doesn't answer but looks at Marshall like, mind your business to Marshall and says, "Let it go, man. The two walk off with Satch limping."

TOWER MUSIC, DAYTON, OHIO - AFTERNOON - WINTER 1973

Two weeks later, the band without Junie is at a press release for their fourth album titled "Ecstasy." Marshall turns to Pee Wee and says, Greg said Junie's nowhere to be found. In ten minutes, we gonna do the shoot without him. "While Marshall asked the question, Junie was standing in a recording booth in Detriot at Westbound Records looking real nervous with a pair of state-of-the-art headphones on his head. Junie leans over to the microphone and says, I don't know about this? Just one song, right? Herb sitting in the control room next to his producer gives Junie a thumbs up.

In the next show, Pee Wee gets drunk, holding his bottle, and starts arguing with anyone who walks by. Satch and Greg walk over to Pee Wee, and Satch taps Greg saying he got it. Satch walks up to Pee Wee, and Pee Wee lets him have it while Greg laughs. Satch, pissed off, gets up in Pee Wee's face and says, "This motherfucker don't think we serious! Our second gold album! You need to look at the part. Your dusty-looking ass"…" Pee Wee punches Satch, then Greg jumps in between them and grabs Satch. Pee Wee runs to grab his trumpet. He rushes back swinging his trumpet, missing Satch but hits Greg dead in the chest. Pee Wee falls to the floor drunk, but before Greg can react, Satch grabs Greg and says, "Greg, hold on, 'he's a drunk man. 'Ain't no sense in starting nothing." Satch helps Pee Wee up, and Greg comes over to help as well. The next morning, Greg sits at table with the newspaper while drinking his coffee. Pee Wee comes over to Greg and sits next to him and is as sympathetic as he could be, saying, "Greg, how you feeling, man?"

Greg, with the newspaper still up, answers him, "I'm good. Pee Wee, you were a fool last night. I wanted to slap the shit out of you." Greg drops the newspaper, and Pee Wee says, "I was drunk. I'm sorry, man! You know I never try and hurt you." Greg trying to get rid of Pee Wee, says, "Don't sweat it." Greg raises his newspaper, trying to get rid of him. Still, Pee Wee gently takes the newspaper out of Greg's hands, feeling Greg doesn't believe him. He looks him in the eye and says, "I mean that brother, I apologize with all my heart, man!" Greg smiles and genuinely accept the apology saying, "It's cool, man, we family" The two hug each other, then slap each other five, laughing it off.

Junie walks into a little music store in Soho, NYC. He walks up to the Store Employee, a white 23-year-old native New Yorker, tech nerd. Inside the shop, you see old-fashioned drum machines and used drums, guitars, etc. The Store employee greets Junie right away as he walks in, touching the equipment. "What's shaking? How may I help you?" Junie, not looking too impressed, replies, "I'm looking for a new synth sound. I got something stuck in my head. I gotta get out." The store employee gestures to Junie to follow him to the other showcase. Then he says, "I have a few things you're gonna want to see."

The store employee reaches into the showcase that he's at and grabs a 1971 Keio/Korg Checkmate drum machine. He places it on the table, smiles at Junie, and says, "The Keio/Korg...." Junie shaking his head no, finishes the sentence, wiping the smile off the employee's face. "Checkmate drum machine. I got two of those. I don't think you get me. I gotta split anyway." Junie turns around, ready to walk off, and the store employee says... "Holy shit, Hold on, Pain... The Ohio Players?" Junie turns around with a smile. The store employee replies, "Man, do I have something for you to see. Hold on." The Store Employee walks to the store's backroom and returns with a box, walking back with a silly grin. He walks over to the counter and places the box with his arms folded, shaking his head yes. Junie, never seeing this name on the box, says, "What's this?" the employee, seeing this has sparked Junie's interest folds his arms then says confidently, "The Arp Pro Soloist! The next level in studio recordings synth sounds."

Junie's eyes light up, and he says, "Plug it up. Let me see." The store employee starts to open the box and starts to hook up the equipment. Junie, more relaxed, says, "Man, I started playing around four. I was in a baby church choir, playing the piano. Man, my feet could barely touch the floor. So my only option was to stamp out the funk using the sustain

pedal of the piano. The funk groove was awesome...
I was the choir director and the orchestra conductor
in high school, so arranging a song is easy for me."

The Store Employee plugs in the speaker, and it
makes a weird sound. Junie looks like this is the
sound in his head. Junie excitedly turns the ARP
PRO SOLOIST to him, looking at the buttons. Then
he plays the grove to Funky Worm, and Junie
smiles while he bops his head to the melody.

The band is in their Westbound Recording studio in
the booth hooking microphones to their instruments.
Greg sets a microphone up to his snare, and then he
checks the two overhead microphones.

Inside Greg's bass drum is an inner tube from a car
tire folded in a square. Pee Wee, Marshall, and
Sugarfoot are off to the side tuning their mic'ed
instruments. All of a sudden, you hear banging on
the glass, and you see Junie and Apple. Junie is
holding up the Arp Soloist. Junie and Apple are
wearing matching black furs. Then Apple waves to
Marshall, smiling from ear to ear. Marshall turns to
Pee Wee and says, "Junie's going to have us up all
night! See that look on his face. Watch he's going to
come wit, we going to do something easy today,
watch!" Pee Wee smiles as he gets ready to say
something. Junie walks in, saying, "OK, OK, let's
do something easy today." Marshall and Pee Wee

start to laugh, and Pee Wee says, "This motherfucker." Junie pops in the door and says, "Everybody mic'ed up? Greg, always needing to be the authority, taps Satch and says, "Junie, how many changes we got this time?" Junie being slick, rubs Greg's ego saying, "Greg, you're going to love this. I see that new Zickos drum set. Sweet, now y'all follow my lead."

Everyone goes to their instruments, Junie on the Keyboard plays the groove to Funky Worm, and everyone's eyes light up and join in playing behind him. After a few minutes of everyone playing together, Junie jumps up from the keyboard and yells, "THAT'S IT!!! Satch, remember that intro I told you about?" Satch, smirking, nods his head. "Yes." Junie walks out of the room fast, then goes into the control booth and says something to the engineer. Everyone in the band stops looking at Junie through the glass as he points at them through the glass. Sugarfoot looks at Pee Wee and says, "We in for it tonight!" Pee Wee jumps in, saying, "Yeah, another long fuckin night."

Pee Wee shaking his head, takes a drink of wine, then Junie walks back into the room and heads straight to the keyboard. Junie's followed by Apple waves while smiling at Marshall as she walks into the room. Greg shakes his head as Junie walks by, and Junie doesn't look up at him. Suddenly, Junie points to Greg, and Greg says, "OK ON 1! 4, 3, 2, 1." Greg starts to play the drums while Junie plays the groove, and Marshall plays the bass behind him. Apple hits the mic in front of Junie, and she says, "She's here, Mr. Johnson."

Apple ducks her head down and tiptoes out of the room in a hurry. Satch steps up to the mic in front of him and sings with soul, "Thank you very much, Granny, they're expecting you... You're a little late, So come right this way. Step right in, OK." Marshall looks at Satch, surprised. Junie closes his eyes, falling into character answering Satch using his Granny Voice says, "What? Say it now? Oh. Say it now, say it now. Ahem! The Ohio Players and I are gonna tell you about a worm. He's the funkiest worm in the world, alright. Sing it, Clarence. Satch comes up to his mic singing, "There's a worm in the ground, yes there is" Junie replies, "That's right." Satch answers, "He's six feet long." Junie jumps back in, saying, "Six feet long." Satch replies, "He only comes around," Junie, in Grannies voice, says, "When he wants to get down But when he comes out of his hole, He sounds something like this."

Junie hits the switch, on the Arp Pro Soloist turning it on, and he starts to play a crazy-sounding keyboard part, and everyone looks at him amazed. Apple and the engineer start bopping their heads to the funky sound while everyone follows Junie playing to this funky groove. Junie hits the mic saying, "Oh, that's funky. Like nine cans of shaving powder, that's funky, Alright. Sing it again, Clarence" Satch gets soulful and sings, "And through all the land, yeah" The Junie in Grannie's voice comes back in saying, "Yeah," Satch sings, "He plays in a band." Junie, still in character, says, "Plays in a band." Satch, with his eyes closed, gets into a real zone during this bar. Singing ever so soulfully says, "Plays guitar without any hands... Pretty good, I might add." Marshall and Pee Wee both look at each other amazed. Junie seeing this goes into his Grannie character and belts out, "Yeah, when he grabs his guitar and starts to pluck, everybody wants to get up and dance." The band could see the engineer and Apple through the glass bopping their heads in a mean grove, feeling the music in the control room. Later that night in Westbound Recording Studio, the song "Funky Worm" by the Ohio Players plays. The band with Junie behind the control board is in the studio playing back a song they just made, looking very satisfied. The engineer is sleeping on the couch while Marshall and Pee Wee point at him as Junie wore out another engineer.

Everyone in the room, including a set of groupies hanging on the side, looks very pleased as they listen and bop their heads to the beat. The Record

Label's owner Armen Boladian (Mid 30's), walks in the room looking serious, and he points to Junie at the controls saying, "Play that back!" Junie plays the song back, and everyone in the room's heads starts to bop again. Armen, still looking serious, puts his hand up to gesture to stop Junie. Then Armen smiles at Junie breaking the tension in the room, and he says, "Fellas, we got a hit!" Apple kisses Junie, and everyone in the room starts to celebrate. Oh, was Armen right? This record chart was #1 on billboard music charts in 1973. This record puts the Players in the game and makes Junie a bigger target. Following the success of "Funky Worm," the label Westbound gave Junie a brand-new Rolls Royce along with his solo album deal.

JUNIE AND APPLE'S NEW HOUSE - EVENING - SUMMER 1973

Apple and Junie argue in the living room, and Apple throws a vase at Junie, just missing him and hitting the wall. Then she yells, "YOU NOT GOING TO FUCK THIS UP! AND I LIKE MARSHALL AND PEE WEE! QUIT THE BAND? NEGRO, YOU CRAZY!"

Junie looks at her unafraid and like she is a piece of shit. Apple seeing Junie's look on his face, breaks down. She tries to open her arms, gesturing to give me a hug walking towards Junie. Looking at Apple with malice, Junie puts his hand out to stop her in her tracks and says, "Matter fact, pack your shit! I don't want you no more! Junie is getting too big for some bitch slowing him down!" Junie looks her up and down like she's a piece of shit. Apple puts her head down like a child being scolded. Junie getting even more wicked, says, "Oh, you think I'm playing! I get back, and I'll see you here. I'll throw your ass out myself!" Junie pimp walks to the front door and slams it loud. Hours later, Apple is drinking a liquor bottle; distraught, she leaves a note on the coffee table. Then she grabs her bags, turns the lights out, and walks out, touching the door as if it's the last time.

Three days later, in the rehearsal studio, Marshall walks in the room with a paper in his hand, looking pissed. Marshall heads straight for Pee Wee and says, "So Junie not coming again? Is it me, or is motherfucker acting real fuckin funny lately?" Pee Wee, feeling something's up, says, "I know he done missed three shows. We came too far for this bullshit! Marshall calls Apple, see if he's there bullshitting." Pee Wee and Marshall walk over to the phone, and Marshall dials the number. It rings, and an older lady answers the phone crying, and her voice is cracking, "Hello?" Marshall, hearing this, changes his tune and says, "Hello, can I speak to Apple?"

Sobbing and yelling, the elderly lady replies, "APPLE'S GONE! SHE DONE KILLED HERSELF! OVER SOME DAMN BOY NAMED JUNIE. (Sobbing) She drove her car right off the bridge." You hear the phone slam and then the dial tone. Marshall puts the phone down and looks at Pee Wee shaking his head. Pee Wee says, "What?" Marshall replies, "Apple's dead! She drove her car off the bridge. The lady on the phone said it has something to do with Junie." Pee Wee looks at Marshall, confused, then Marshall tilts his head to the side, looking just as confused. At the Same Time, Junie is in Detroit at his solo album photoshoot. Junie is taking pictures, sitting hugged up with the same model Pat Running Bear Evans from the album "Pain." The lights start to flash from the camera's flash, and all the magazine's reporters start to write while some shake their heads in disgust. Junie calls Marshall and asks Pee Wee to come by his new pad. Junie opens the door to an angry-looking Marshall and Pee Wee. Junie playing it real cool, says, "Pee Wee, Marshall, c'mon in." Pee Wee using his left arm, nudges Junie out the way, and they walk right past him, saying, "Man, watch out!" Junie, with a big old smile, says, "Have a seat." Marshall and Pee Wee looked around, amazed at how nice Junie's new house was, and Marshall says "Damn! Nice crib, man! I got to check the books. We must be paying your little black ass too much."

Pee Wee sees some nice-looking weed on the table and reaches for it while looking at Junie. Junie ignores Pee Wee, turning to Marshall smiling, and Junie says, "Well, there is something I gotta tell the band, but since y'all here." Marshall passing Pee Wee some rolling papers says, "OK, spit it out." Junie stands up, pleased with a big silly grin on his face, and says, "Marshall, I did record an album, and I want you and Pee Wee in my band?" Pee Wee jumps up pissed off and says, "Hot damn!" Marshall, looking completely baffled, says, "You sure you want to do that?" Not seeing the reaction he thought he would get, Junie changes his angel, saying, "Yeah, Marshall, I want my own bread. Don't you?"

Pee Wee, mad as hell, tries to inhale the joint, but it's out, so he passes it to Marshall with his lighter and says, "Man, you might as well step the fuck off!" Marshall lights the joint and inhales, shaking his head. Then he says, "We gonna smoke yo shit tho." Pee Wee steaming reaches for the joint, saying, "Damn right, pass that! Man, you realize what this group has been through? Junie looks at Marshall as he always admired Marshall, but

Marshall, not falling for it, says, "Man, I brought you in the band, and this is how you repay the love?" Junie realizing what he did, sits back on the couch and puts his head down.

TOWNHOUSE BUFFALO NEW YORK - DUSK - FALL 1973

Marshall, Sugarfoot, Pee Wee, and Satch are sitting in Satch's living room, being real quiet. Then Greg walks in the room and says, "Well, I called Westbound, and he's not lying." Marshall slaps a stack of magazines off of the sofa table, and then Satch stands up and whips out a 357-magnum looking serious, and he says, "OK, where y'all shit! I'm not losing shit. Imma make that motherfucker sing! Marshall slams his hand on the coffee table, then stands up and yells, "LOOK, NO MORE BRINGING PEOPLE IN FROM OUTSIDE IT'S…." Sugarfoot playing with his guitar, lifts his head, interrupts Marshall, and says, "Getting old! That's what the fuck it is!" Marshall whips out an ounce of weed, taking out some and leaving the bag on the table. Reluctantly one by one, everyone grabs a little and starts to roll a joint. They start to smoke, and Greg putting his joint down, says, "On a serious note. I need to know something right now; did anyone know bout Junie fuckin us over?". Marshall pointing to Pee Wee, says, "Shit, after we went from seven hundred night gigs to twenty thou a night after "Funky Worm," come on. Me and Pee Wee was the only ones that caught on to that bullshit." Satch stands up and looks at Sugarfoot to answer. Sugarfoot looks at Satch to say beat it, then Greg says, "OK, we gotta get a new singer."

Sugarfoot, pissed off, is looking down and away when he looks back up, everyone staring at him, and he says, "What?" Marshall, smiling and laughing, says, "You gonna sing!" Pee Wee puts his hand on Sugarfoot's shoulder. Satch bends down in front of Sugarfoot facing him, and he says Foots, we tired of bringing in new singers, so tag you're it. Then Satch stands up looking at the band, like a coach that just won the Superbowl, and he says, "It's time to stand out above da rest!" Sugarfoot smiles, taking his double-neck guitar out the box for Satch taking a picture.

Meanwhile, Marshall confidently holds his bass while looking at himself in a mirror with a turban on his head. At the same time, everyone in the room is pointing at and laughing at him. Pee Wee is turning his trumpet bell up so loud; everyone holds their ears. The band except Satch is standing together with their new image while Satch sets the camera and runs in the picture. After the picture, Satch, standing looking at everyone interacting with each other, says, "Now this is the beginning of a

146

winning formula. The Ohio Players!" The energy in
the room was monumental.

BILLY'S CHURCH - AFTERNOON - FALL 1973

Satch and Marshall are sitting in Satch's Cadillac
outside in the parking lot of a church waiting on an
eighteen-year-old Billy Beck to get out of the
church in Youngstown, Ohio. Satch looking
exciting turns to Marshall and says, "Marshall, all
we need is this kid on Keyboards to get back on the
road."

Suddenly, the church lets out, and you see some
pretty young women walking by the car, checking
out Satch and Marshall. Looking at the ladies Satch
and Marshall never see Billy walk up to the car.
Then Billy, with the heavy country accent, says,
"Hey." Both Marshall and Satch Jump, then Satch
says, "What the hell... oh my bad, pardon me, and
he kisses his cross on his neck. Then Satch says,
"You ready?" Billy glances over to an older couple
looking at the car-mad, as you know. Then Billy
jumps in the car and says, "Drive!" Satch pulls off
fast while the lady in the older couple pumps her
fist shakes her head, praying as her husband
consoles her. Billy is in the backseat getting
undressed as Marshall and Satch laugh at him.

HAMILTON HOSPITAL OHIO, HOSPITAL ROOM - DAY - WINTER 73

Pee Wee walks into Greg's hospital room in Hamilton Hospital to see Greg looking bad in his hospital bed. Pee Wee places his hand on Greg's shoulder, Greg seeing his brother puts a smile on his face, and Pee Wee says, "Greg, how you been, man?" Greg, with his voice a little froggy, says, "Well, it looks like I got diabetes. Pee Wee pulls a chair closer to the bed and sits down, looking at Greg dead in his eyes, concerned. Then he says, "DIABETES! Damn, sorry to hear that." Greg sits up and says, "This Band is my life, my family. I hate to leave y'all like this. I had to go to the doctor cause something didn't feel right. The last time we played, my leg felt like it was gonna fall off." Pee Wee looks Greg in the eye, and being as empathetic as he could be, he says, "Damn! I came to tell you we gotta move on, but that's some heavy shit you just laid on me." Greg smirks and says, "I already figured that. But you man! No matter what went down, you always kept it real, and I love you, brother."

Without saying a word, Pee Wee puts his head down, and a tear falls from his eye. Greg seeing this, is moved as well and opens his arms for a hug from his friend.

RECORDING STUDIO, CHICAGO - NIGHT - JANUARY 1974

The Ohio Players leave Westbound Records due to accounting and Royalty issues and sign with Mercury Records. Who at the time was looking to explore the R&B market. One of Mercury Records Owners was not convinced the group would be profitable, but he took a chance after making a bet with his label's president Irvin Steinburg saying that the band would not succeed.

The band is in Paragon Recording Studio in their gobo's facing Satch. Satch, looking very serious, starts looking over to Robert "Kuumba" Jones Billy Beck, then James "Diamond" Williams, and says, "By now y'all realized every song we made was in a jam." Billy nods his head, yeah while Diamond and Kuumba look lost. Satch looks at Sugarfoot and says, "Foots, Skintight!" Sugarfoot gives Satch the thumbs up.

Marshall leans over to Billy, who is looking confused, and whispers. "Skintight is the song title, and foots is going to make a whole song to that one word on the groove. Billy, amazed, says, "What? You serious, I got to see this." Satch clears his throat to get Marshall and Billy's attention, then with a strong, demanding tone, he yells, "HOW MANY PEOPLE IN THE ROOM?" Everyone responds except Diamond and Billy as they look lost. "EIGHT," Satch sounding like an army drill sergeant, says, "HOW MANY MINDS IN THE ROOM?"

Kuumba, Diamond and Billy look like deer in headlights. Marshall, Pee Wee, Merv, and Sugarfoot answer, "ONE MIND!!!" Pee Wee starts to shake his head, seeing Diamond looking mesmerized by Satch. Satch tones it down, taking his shades off, looking everyone in their eyes, says, "OK, let's welcome Diamond to the band as our new drummer. I took this position as Manager, wanting to push the envelope. I told Mercury we have 40 songs ready to go, then promised Mercury we'd have the album to them in two weeks! And that was eleven days ago! I know this has been hard but, this is what you wanted, Right? So, let's lay this last one down."

In the gobo next to Pee Wee, Marshall looks at him and says, "This motherfucker's high as hell. We finished seven songs, flew back to New York to do a show every night for eight days. Shit, we got a show tonight in New York! This motherfucker better have something stronger than coke tonight."

Satch points over to Marshall and Pee Wee, gesturing to get to their places, then says, "On 1! 4,3,2,1." The band starts the song Skintight by the

Ohio Players. About 15 seconds into the song, Marshall waits for Pee Wee's horn part but doesn't hear it. Marshall looks over to see Pee Wee knocked out in the gobo next to him; then, everybody stops playing. Marshall, next to Pee Wee, shakes him, saying, "Yo! Wake up, man." Pee Wee wakes up wiping dribble from his mouth and says, "Marshall, how the hell you think you could fit in my pants? You wanted this motherfucking gig, huh?"

The studio falls out laughing, and Satch's face gets serious and says, "OK... jokes take time! And time is money! Then under his breath, he says, "My money motherfuckers." Marshall hears Satch and shakes his head in disgust.

SOUL TRAIN TV STUDIO - DAY - NOVEMBER 9, 1974

The band is at Soultrain on-stage ready to perform "Skintight" by the Ohio Players. Dressed in gold outfits looking stylish, Satch is in the center of the stage. At the same time, Sugarfoot comes out with his double-neck guitar from behind Satch.

Marshall, far left, dropping an Oh-So-Funky Bass Riff. Pee Wee and Satch step up-front with their horns, keeping the crowd mesmerized by their new sound and look. All you see is a sea of Afro's bopping, doing the bump and all kinds of different dance moves till the song ends. As the crowd gives a standing ovation and Don Cornelius walks into the middle of the audience up to the stage saying, "We're back with the fabulous Ohio Players, I'll like to begin with asking Clarence Satchell, better known as Satch, to introduce the members individually" Then Don passes the mic to Satch up on the Stage, "First of all Mr. Marshall Jones Capricorn.

Pee Wee stands next to him, the Leo, Mr. Marvin Pierce better known as Merv, Cancer, Jim Diamond next to him that's his name, Aries. Next to me is Billy Beck, better known as Silly Billy the Gemini, and Next to him is a Pisces, Sugar. He likes that name Silly Billy cause he got a tune out, and yours truly Satch Aries. Don't get off on it. Get into it." The Crowd cheers and Don says, "We'd like to offer our congratulations on an absolutely sensational album, Manly the Skintight album. Congratulation on a platinum sales and a million-seller with the Skintight single." Satch, smiling, says, "I didn't believe it; I don't know what to say?" Don being coy, says, "Just take the money and put it in the bank." The audience cheers, then Don points the mic to a foxy number, and she says, "My name is Sherrel Davis, and I'd like to know Clarence. How long have you been playing saxophone, and do you play any other instruments?" "Uh, Do I play other Instruments, Of course, I do?

As you can see, I play four instruments, and so does the entire horn section, but I've been playing for twelve years." Don points his long skinny microphone at a member of the audience. Bobby, a young brother with a really nice afro, steps up to ask a question "My name is Bobby Washington, and I'd like to know, How did the group get started?" Satch smirks, standing next to Don, then he answers the question, "We from the same town, but we all got together because we got thrown out of other groups. The crowd laughs at his charismatic humor.

Don points his mic to another male member of the studio audience, and he says, "My name is Tyron Swan, and I'd like to know Who wrote the song Skin Tight, and did you think it was gonna be as big as it was, I mean is?" Satch working with the audience, says, "We didn't know how big it was going to be. We are all jointly responsible for anything we do. We do it as a unit. We record it and put it out as a unit. Therefore, we all share writer and producer credits." Then Satch looks at Don and says, "There's a lot of fellas up here." The audience claps while some get more engaged in the conversation. Then Don points his mic to a female member of the studio audience, and she says, "How

do you classify yourselves?" Don remembering
what Satch said, he points the mic to Sugarfoot, and
Sugarfoot answers, "Smart." The comment arouses
the attention of the female audience.

CHICAGO RECORDING STUDIO - NIGHT - WINTER 1974

The band is in Paragon Recording Studio playing
The Instrumental to "Fire" by the Ohio Players.
Stevie Wonder walking by the band's studio
session, hears the band jamming the groove to
"Fire." Stevie excitedly comes in, saying, "You can
name this song anything. It's a hit. You can name it
Rock Papers Scissors. It's smokin; it's smokin'!"

Satch looks at Sugarfoot like you hear that. Then
Satch says, "Fire! We gon call it "Fire!" Stevie
Wonder smiles and walks out, and Satch takes a real
big hit of coke, and he passed it to Marshall. Then
he grabs a bottle of champagne and sprays it on
some female groupies in the studio and yells,
"ANYONE SAY FIRE!!!!" The female groupies
start yelling; they run out of the room, and Satch
follows them, spraying champagne. Let's just say
the players were on fire, closing out Phil Donahue's
last show in Dayton, Ohio, and getting the key to
the city from Mayor James McGee on National Tv.

154

"Skintight" goes number one on the US Billboard Top Soul LP's, and with the album's release, it would almost outsell every one of the Ohio Players' works combined. Later that night, during a break, Marshall and Pee Wee are outside drinking a bottle of Pee Wee's favorite wine, "Dom Perignon." Then Pee Wee looks at Marshall with a serious face and says, "You realize what's going on?" Marshall, high and confused, says, "What?" Pee Wee starts to smile then says, "We don't have to worry bout paying bills no more. WE MADE IT!!!" Marshall starts to smile along with Pee Wee then says, "Sixteen-year man." The two hugs and Marshall break down and cry in relief as money is no longer an issue (They made it.)

The Ohio Players creating major attention for their brand forces other labels to release albums in a hurry, trying to capitalize off the success of the "Ohio Players." Capitol Records would release the album "The Ohio Players." A month before the anticipated release of "Fire" by the "Ohio Players." Then Westbound Records released old left-over studio works of the "Ohio Players" Climax was released in October 1974.

Climax is the sixth studio album released by the "Ohio Players" At this time. The Band is signed to Mercury Records.

MERCURY RECORDS RECORDING STUDIO,
CHICAGO -

The record "Love Rollercoaster" by the Ohio
Players plays. The band and all the record producers
and executives from Mercury Records are bopping
their heads to the beat. While the producer plays
back their new song, "Love Rollercoaster," the
engineer, looking confused, stops the track and
says, "SHIT! We got loud screams on the track. It
blended in so good I didn't notice it." Robin
McBride stands up and says, "Play it back."

The producer plays the part where Billy Beck
screams, emulating a girl riding a rollercoaster.
Robin, with a big silly smile, excitedly says,
"WHOA, THAT GOTTA STAY! Believe me. I'll
call my publicist, and she'll find a way to spin this."
Then he walks out of the room with a big smile on
his face.

The next week Marshall and Pee Wee sit at a light
in Marshall's Porsche 911 S, in front of a
newspaper stand in the middle of Times Square.
They see four teenage white girls running up to the
stand in a hurry. They purchase a newspaper and
form a huddle, turning to an article saying the
scream on "Love Rollercoaster" is a woman being
murdered. The four teenage white girls run into a
record store in front of the newsstand. Pee Wee taps

Marshall to drive as he's in a daze, and the two drive off.

BACKSTAGE IN A NIGHTCLUB IN NYC

The band is backstage in a club in New York, and a young white tour promoter is in the room talking to Satch. Satch barely catches eye contact with him and is not interested in what he has to say.

The Tour Promoter being persistent, says, "Look after what you guys did on the last tour. You gotta consider this Earth Wind & Fire tour?" Satch starts to bite at the bait, pausing with his hand to his chin. Then Satch looks over to Marshall, nodding his head of approval, then he says, "I know the fans been asking for this, but… Then Satch snaps halfway through his sentence looking over to the promoter like he did something wrong, and he says, "The Ohio Players don't open for no one! What the fuck we look like?" the tour promoter being the weasel he was, took another shot. "OK... how about more money?" Satch looks at Marshall, and Marshall says, "Make it a lot more, and we in!"

LONDON SOUTH END A PRIVATE AIRPORT - NOON - SUMMER

With "Fire" now going platinum and still number one going on its fifth week. One of Mercury

Records' owners flew the band to Heathrow by Concord after the owner lost his bet. The Mercury Record Owner excitedly walks on the plane, saying, "Come on, I got someone waiting to meet y'all." The Record owner walking off stops and says, "Oh, I booked you guy a show at the Hammersmith Apollo in England."

The band starts to cheer, knowing what a big deal it is to play there. As the players make it to the runway, they unexpectedly get ushered towards three white Rolls Royce limos by two very sexy female stewardesses. From out of the limo in the middle, Elton John steps out with a big smile gesturing for the band to get in the limos.

The band sees who it is, then smiles and gets in the limos. Marshall, Pee Wee, and Sugarfoot in one of the limo's seeing very expensive champagnes in the glass bar. So, Marshall thinking he knows a little something and just being curious, says, "Sugar pass me that clear bottle of Champagne." Sugar shakes his head, moving slowly, knowing Marshall, but Marshall hits him with the face, and Sugarfoot reluctantly passes it and Marshall. With his face made up, Marshall does not look impressed and says, "This some cheap shit! Champagne needs to be put in dark bottles." Pee Wee grabs it trying to shut Marshall up. The driver lowers the partition and says, "Louis Roederer is very expensive, top shelf, have a taste."

Pee Wee popping the top says, "Already on it, boss." Then he pours a drink in a glass and tastes it.

Pee Wee, looking amazed, passes Marshall a glass, and he starts to pour. Marshall takes a drink and looks over to Sugarfoot like, you gotta try this. Pee Wee sees this; then he passes it over to Sugarfoot with a glass while the driver raises the partition. The three limos pull up to one of Elton John's houses in London.

The players are in Elton John's den, getting to know each other and sitting around drinking and talking Jive. Sugarfoot and Elton take a real liking to each other while laughing and joking around. Sugarfoot says, "Nah, Elton, you the man! I'm drinking milk every day trying to be like you."

Elton stands up in front of Sugarfoot and replies, "Come on, Sugar! You guys are absolutely groovy! So, you knocked me off my #1 spot. Oh, come now, I'll take a drink to that. The band stands up. Come now, raise your glasses. To the Ohio Players, may your success continue!" They take a drink, and Elton smiles at Sugarfoot and says, "Sugar, I have a guitar part I would like you to check out. Do you mind?" Sugarfoot stands up, saying, "Come on, man, it be my pleasure!"

The two leave the room, and the rest of the players looks at each other in amazement. Marshall stands over Satch puts his glass up to make a toast. Satch says, "What's that for?" Marshall replies, "To pulling it off!" Satch stands up looking his brother Marshall in the eyes and then Satch looks over to Pee Wee to join the toast. The three make a toast to their journey and having two platinum albums in one year.

Sugarfoot and Elton come back into the room, and Elton sends for the Limos, and the players start to realize that Elton is their host. Elton looking at the band, says, "One of the Rolls Royce Limos are for you guys, oh, and the Owner of Mercedes has paid for your hotel." Later that night, the Ohio Players performed at Hammersmith Odeon, rocking the crowd. Then they headed straight back to the airport, flying to the Netherlands, and when the players touched down, we were met with nine Mercedes limos, one for each member.

The Mercedes limos were waiting for the band's most anticipated meeting. Still, before that, the players needed to freshen up so the drivers would drive in a caravan to the Pulitzer Hotel in Amsterdam. The next morning the band heads downstairs to see another fleet of limos waiting to take them to their very important meeting.

As the fleet of limos approached their designation, the players couldn't believe the enormity of the owner's dwelling. At first glance, it looked like the band was pulling up to a church with a thatched roof. As the players entered, they were led through the atrium to an enormous dining room with a very large table that just looked like royalty. As the players get seated, servants start to bring trays of various expensive dishes. The players enjoying their meal were stopped by a grand announcement of the owner by his butler. The Band looks to see a small man with a great big smile on his face greeting the group. The first words out of his mouth were, "Let me get a look at y'all. I couldn't believe a black group could sell so many records. I told Irving not to sign the group. Shit, I bet him you wouldn't make it, but here's to being wrong." He puts his glass up, and everyone joins in for a toast.

The Players' last stop would be a nightclub in the French riviera. The Ohio Players without Marshall rushed out of the two limousines, excited to close out their overseas tour.

As they make it to the door, the security guards put their hands out, gesturing to stop. Satch at the front of the Band says, "We the Ohio Players." The doorman standing beside a huge security guard waves his hand, gesturing to get rid of them to one of the security guards.

Then a limo with Marshall in it pulls up. Marshall comes out with his turban and a mean strut, looking like a black prince on his way to the door. The doorman and security see Marshall walking toward the door and bow their heads while holding the door open for Marshall Stach, and the Band seeing this, yell, "WE WITH HIM!" holding the door open for Marshall.

Nineteen-Seventy-Five at Midnight Special, the Players and Wolfman Jack are on-stage. The Players wearing shiny rhinestone jean suites, with the arms cut off. Then Wolfman Jack walks to the front of the stage and announces the Ohio Players saying, "Oh my, it's so nice to have the Ohio Players back, you know I promised Helen I'll have The Ohio Players back. It's her favorite group, you see! It makes her howl. It makes her dance and do crazy things with her tail! EVERYBODY, LET'S WELCOME "THE OHIO PLAYERS!" The Players performs "Love Rollercoaster" Satch steps in front and talks to the audience and cameras as the song starts, "Rollercoaster, ah.... up, down, all-round, don't tell me I wanna ride." The studio audience live on national TV goes crazy, and the booking kept rolling in.

MERCURY RECORDS, CHICAGO - DAY - SPRING 1975

In the background, the song "Honey" by the Ohio Players plays. The band is standing over Playboy model Esther Cordette as they pour honey all over her naked body, and Marshall and Pee Wee's eyes damn near pop out of their sockets.

Satch Walks in front of Pee Wee and Marshall, smiling from ear to ear, saying, "I told you we're raising the bar this album, huh?" Pee Wee looks down towards his privates, saying, "Yeah, which bar? Goddamn!" Satch shaking his head, says, "Put your tongues back in your mouth, we gotta take these pics in the next room... man, c'mon."

The band is in the main studio, with all of Mercury Records Executives having pictures taken with their Platinum plaques for "Fire" as Jet magazine takes pictures of the Players. After the pictures, two sexy waitresses serve everyone glasses of wine. Robin McBride, Vice President of artist and repertoire for Mercury Records, says, "OK, everyone put your glass up, this is to "Fire" taking the number 1 spot!! To The Ohio Players!" The cameras start to flash, and all of a sudden, you hear walkie-talkies and commotion in the hallway. Everyone stops, and Satch opens the door, and you see two Paramedics walking past the door.

Satch and Marshall look at each other, then they walk out the door towards the commotion. As Marshall and Satch enter the room, they make their way to playboy model Esther Cordette stuck to the plexiglass (due to the hot lights and honey.)

One of the paramedics tries to lift her off the plexiglass as she yells in pain. The second paramedic started to pour warm water on her arm, barely freeing it. The two paramedics seeing this, start to pour the warm water all over her as she lets out loud screams as they separate each body part. Marshall standing next to Satch, is grossed out. Seeing the raw flesh still stuck to the plexiglass. They start to walk out, and Esther screams, and Marshall cringes, then shakes his head.

The Ohio Players' third consecutive platinum album "Honey" goes to the Grammys and wins in the category of Best Album Package and wins its equivalent in France. Honey's album cover was the Ohio Players most erotic cover, with a nude side shot of playboy model Esther Cordette dripping wet of honey more than help sell their album.

Leaving a Network studio after finishing up an interview, the players are outside with the interviewing host Stacey, in the late '20s, a very attractive black female Journalist talking with everyone in the band except Marshall. Stacey smiling, turns to Satch to ask him a question. "That was an amazing interview. Where's the guy with the turban?" Satch points behind her, and as she turns around, Marshall kisses her in the mouth, and Stacey says, "No, you didn't?" Marshall replies, "Yes, I did." The two caught up in the moment, paused for a while, smiling. Marshall takes Stacey's hand, and the two walk out hugging each other and laughing while Marshall whispers in her ear.

HOUSE PARTY IN OLD NEIGHBORHOOD - DAY -SUMMER 1975

Satch drives his two-toned silver & black Stutz Blackhawk down a block in the Players' old neighborhood. Where we see little kids chasing his car down the street, and almost every other house has a band practicing in a garage. As Satch reaches the middle of the block, you see a row of top-end cars, a Yellow Lamborghini Countach, a Red Ferrari 512, a diamond Silver Porsche 911 S, and all the band members standing in front by the cars talking to old friends from the neighborhood. Satch gets out, and a young lady standing next to Marshall shaking her head, says, "All da money in the world can't change dat negro. I bet you he's still an asshole!"

As she says that, they see Satch looking at some sexy female groupies running up to his car while he totally ignores two kids trying to get an autograph from him. The young lady shakes her head and walks off, and Marshall says, "That's your cousin." She keeps walking, totally ignoring Marshall.

STACH'S HOUSE DAYTON OHIO - AFTERNOON - SUMMER 1975

August, nineteen-seventy-five, the Ohio Players show their true musical talent releasing their first single off the album Honey titled "Sweet Sticky Thing" and grabbing major national attention. Satch and Pee Wee are sitting in Satch's office doing lines of cocaine on his desk, getting high when the fax machine rings. Satch gets up to get the fax. Satch stops dead in his tracks and looks at the fax, smiling.

Then he shows it to Pee Wee, and the two smile as they both simultaneously snort lines of cocaine, then they sit back with big stupid smiles on their faces. Sitting on top of the desk in between the two is a one million dollar offer for a tour with Earth Wind & Fire and a tray with cocaine on it. About twenty minutes later, Satch's wife walks in the room, smiling. She wakes Satch and Pee Wee from a deep daze with the Jet Magazine with The Ohio

Players on the cover in her hand. Then Satch points to the offer on the table, and the two hug.

The next day Satch is walking into the Ferrari dealership at the same time Billy gets off a city bus at the Alfa-Romeo dealership. Then Billy rolls out with a brand-new Alfa-Romeo, while Satch leaves the Ferrari dealership with a brand-new Red Ferrari.

With the story brewing about a girl getting stabbed on the song "Love Rollercoaster," the world gets antsy about the "Ohio Players' new record. The press and tabloids have field days worldwide, not to mention the Playboy Model Esther Cordette's incident. Love Rollercoaster goes number one in January nineteen-seventy-six. This makes three platinum albums in two years. The players are now on many major platforms worldwide, demanding constant attention.

Being the treasurer of a multi-million-dollar company, Marshall convinces Satch to rent a plush office in the Grant Deneau Tower in Downtown Dayton, Ohio. With the players doing two-hundred shows per year and selling out the Houston Astros stadium for three nights in a row.

LAGUARDIA AIRPORT, NYC - EVENING - 1976

The "Ohio Players" leave Dayton, Ohio, and flies to LaGuardia Airport in NY. From the airport, they get ushered to a private helicopter, flying to their destination. Marshall points over to the Statue of Liberty, showing Pee Wee. Then Pee Wee looking out the window pointing at the Statue of Liberty's torch, yells "F-I-R-E, New York we coming!"

Marshall and the band catching on, start to laugh but get inspired. The band landed on the top of the World Trade Center. Pee Wee, Marshall, and Sugarfoot on the rooftop make jokes about Sugarfoot's afro blowing from the helicopter's blades as he leaves the helicopter. Then the Players take a private elevator to the Basement then get rushed into a limo. As they pull up to Madison Square Garden, the Players get greeted by a large crowd chanting Sugarfoot's name really loudly. The crowd starts pushing the limo side to side, chanting Sugarfoot and the Ohio Players name, almost flipping it over to get to the Band. Sugarfoot says, "SHIT! They love us, or they want to kill us?"

The limo pulls up in the parking lot, and the driver opens the door fast, and the Players shoot into Madison Square Garden before the fans that made it through the barricades approach fast. After getting in and settling backstage at Madison Square Garden. The soundman walks over to Satch and says the drums didn't make it. As they go, check

168

and find out he's right. The band is backstage in the dressing room, pissed off that Diamond's Drums didn't make it alone with the other equipment.

Satch, pissed, walks out the room towards the room where all the other equipment is to do a second round on inventory. Marshall turns to Pee Wee, and for once, you can see even Pee Wee is bothered, which never happens. Marshall is getting really frustrated as the room is dead quiet, and he says, "All this back and forth bout who's gonna headline, now the fuckin airline loses our drums!" Sugarfoot kicks a box in the corner of the room. Then Pee Wee lifts his head, saying, "Chill out, man! When Earth Wind and Fire get here, we gon turn em on to what's happening! And ask to use their drums." Sugarfoot mad slaps the back of a chair, then walks off, then Sugarfoot turns around, pointing his finger at the Band, and says, "Fuck that! We agreed for them to headline! Now they should do us a solid, that's all I'm saying!" Pee Wee stands up mad and says, "I'm gon ask em!"

Pee Wee taps Diamond, and they both walk out the door to ask Earth Wind & Fire to use their drums. Satch, walking back in the room frustrated, whips out a bag of coke, and Marshall and Sugarfoot smile. Satch walks to sit down at a table, setting lines of coke to snort. Marshall and Sugarfoot join in, taking a seat at the big boy table. Satch snorting

169

a line of cocaine, looks up high and says, "Man, these motherfuckers better not fuck my money up! I mean our money."

Sugarfoot and Marshall both look at each other, hearing what Satch just said. Diamond and Pee Wee come back through the door looking madder than a Motherfucker, and Sugarfoot, concerned, says, "Pee Wee, what the hell's wrong with you. What'd they say?" Pee Wee replies, "No, like them motherfuckers don't want us to perform or something." Sugarfoot jumps out of his chair and throws it at the wall, and says, "What the fuck? After all that!" Marshall jumps in front of Sugarfoot as he's walking towards the door, pissed off.

Marshall grabbing him back, says, "Hold on, Foots! I'm gonna ask them. We need it!" Sugarfoot being sarcastic, replies, "Have fun." Marshall walking in the hallway backstage with his head down talking to himself, runs into Danny Seraphine from the band Chicago. Marshall, with his head down, almost walks by Danny. Danny noticing the distraught Marshall walking with his head down, almost does not recognize it is Marshall. Danny, unsure, says, "Marshall?" Marshall, still with a lot on his mind, barely picks his head up but replies, "Hey Danny, what's up, man?" Danny puts one hand on Marshall's shoulder and slightly bends down to look Marshall in the eye, and he says, "Why so

170

down, my brother?" Marshall semi rambling says, "Man, the airline fuck up, and our drums didn't make it, and."

Danny smiles at Marshall and puts his hand up to gesture stop cutting Marshall off; then he says, "Drums? All our stuff in flight cases downstairs, we stayed overnight just to see this show! Use whatever y'all need. C'mon, I'll help ya." Marshall smiles, slaps Danny five, and they walk off together.

The Players, backstage getting ready to go on, are locked in a huddle, Satch being the bandleader says, "OK! They started it! And we gonna finish it! The Players leave the huddle energized, running out the room to a cheering MSG arena. The Ohio Players are on-stage performing "Love Rollercoaster," rocking the crowd. The crowd screams and chants, "Ohio Players." you see the band leaving the stage to a screaming crowd while the announcer walks on stage, slapping the Players five as they exit the stage. The Announcer looking really hype runs on stage, and he says, "WHOA!!! WHAT A SET! Let's give it up for the baddest set I've ever seen! Up next is Earth Wind and Fire!!!"

The lights get dim, and Earth, Wind, and Fire start to play as the light gets brighter, you see that the people were so tired from dancing to the Ohio

Players Music, they're barely dancing now. Marshall and Sugarfoot look through the curtain, and Sugarfoot sees hardly anyone is dancing, so he points to show Marshall saying, "We killed it!!! They not even dancing!" The next song comes on, and more people start to sit down. Marshall points saying, "Look at the crowd they sitting down, shit, barely dancing!" You see more people sitting down. Let's just say the uptempo songs the Ohio Players came out and rocked the house that night. The next day the Players went back to Dayton and boarded their tour bus to head for St Louis to the Busch Memorial Stadium.

As the bus approaches the stadium gate, the marquee says Earth Wind and Fire and Ohio Players. The Players exit the bus with Satch at the lead, trying to walk past the security guard. He gets stopped by him. The security guard looking like he loves to be the bearer of bad news, condescendingly says, "Whoa, hold on...you can't come in! Sorry, those are my orders!"

Satch looks him in the eye, pissed, and replies in a stern manner, "Orders? Go get da motherfucker givin orders!" The security guard shakes his head no. Pee Wee, confused, says, "But we on the show!" The security guard loving his job at the moment, proudly says, "Not no more!" Satch, not feeling the way he just talked to Pee Wee, steps up in the security guard's face and says, "Well, somebody better have our money then!" Satch's security steps up to enforce what he said, looking tough.

Suddenly the promoter comes from behind the door with a bag full of cash, looking scared, and says, "Here is your money, and sorry for any inconvenience we have caused y'all. Satch, once again, I am very sorry." Satch snatches the money and says, "Shut the fuck up! And everything better be there!" Satch and the Players start to walk off, then Pee Wee starts smiling with a devilish grin and says, "Fuck it! We got paid for nothing. Aye, Marshall, we still got the speakers on the bus?" Marshall smiles at Pee Wee, catching the drift, then he yells to all the people in the parking lot, "CAN ANYONE SAY YARD PARTY!!!" The Players get the fans to help grab some speakers, Amps, etc. From the tour bus to give a free concert in the parking lot. At this time the Players were on top, "On night Marshall meet Mick Jagger backstage at one of our shows in New York. The Rolling Stones had come to see them perform. He was so enamored with Sugarfoot he tells Marshall that he wants to meet him so bad he'll suck his dick if he has to. Sugarfoot wasn't on it, so Mick didn't get to meet him that night.

YACHT PARTY LAKE MICHIGAN - NIGHT - AUGUST 1976

The song "Sweet Sticky Thing" by the Ohio Players plays, come on walk with me. We have to set the ambiance. The Players arrive by limo to a large luxury yacht on Lake Michigan. The Players get out looking clueless as they start to board the yacht. Marshall, the last to walk on the yacht, looks back to see no cars in the parking lot. Then everyone heads inside, and they are ushered to a decked-out ballroom, where all of Mercury Records Label's Executives are waiting to greet them. You see the band shaking hands with the executives as everyone is happy to greet them. When all of a sudden, they hear a loud bus horn blowing over and over. Pee Wee, never the one to hold his tongue, says, "Y'all don't hear that." Everyone not hearing looks confused, then the bus horn starts again. The record executive pats Pee Wee on his shoulder and, with a smile, says horn blowing? "That horn blowing is for the Grammy, three platinum albums, and "-Love Rollercoaster" going #1! Oh, you boys gonna thank me later, come on."

Everyone goes up on deck to see two tour buses loaded with Playboy Bunnies boarding the yacht to entertain the band for three nights. Satch holding a champagne bottle, starts to shake it, then he goes in his pocket looking at Pee Wee and Marshall. Then he whips out a nice-sized bag of coke; they smile with devilish grins. Satch pops the bottle of champagne, spraying it off the yacht while holding a bag of coke in his mouth.

Then Satch grabs the bag of coke from his mouth and says, "Now yall started the real party! I need three of them. that one, that one, and maybe that one. THE OHIO PLAYERS BABY!!!" Satch continues spraying the bottle off the side of the yacht.

They partied for three days straight, having all the pussy and cocaine they wanted. Let's just say the captain didn't even have a chance to sleep in his own quarters two of these nights.

UPSCALE HOTEL IN LA - NIGHT - FALL 1976

Fall Nineteen-Seventy-Six at one of the Ohio Players Concert After-Parties in LA, Satch-looking star-studded, comes out the kitchen with a bowl of coke. More than half of the party jumps for joy and surrounds Satch. Satch being the entertainer, yells, "OK, LINE UP!!! Y'ALL READY TO HOP ON THIS MOTHERFUCKING ROCKET-SHIP, CAUSE WE BOUT TO BLAST OFF 5,4,3,2,1!" The crowd, mostly white, lines up as Satch starts to distribute some fine china. While Marshall and Pee

Wee sit off to the side on a couch with Red Fox. Marshall shaking his head, starts pointing at Satch to show Pee Wee, then he yells for Satch to come over, "Look at this shit. YO SATCH, COME HERE FOR A MINUTE, MY BROTHER!!!"

Satch walks over, feeling himself, and says, "What's shaking jive turkey?" Marshall trying to be stern says, "Where you getting all this bread to entertain all these motherfuckers night after night?" Satch bends down, getting right up in Marshall's face, and says, "Worry bout what you got in your pocket! Don't watch mine! You got me, my brother! Hope we all clear, ya dig!"

Satch looks at Pee Wee (Like so what), knowing that he heard him, and the pimp walks back to two ladies waiting for him. At this time, the Player's work ethic started to decline due to all of the members now getting high, and the drug of choice was cocaine. The Players started to spiral out of control, missing many practices and spending even less time recording.

Marshall at his house with his glass full of wine in the air making a toast to a room full of friends to "Who'd She Coo hitting the #1 spot on "Hot Soul Single!" A lady high on coke and nodding off drops her glass and smiles at Marshall. Then a man sniffing coke on a table hears the glass drop, and he stands up high and swaying with powder on his nose. He puts his glass up to make a toast and falls flat on his face, just missing a glass coffee table. Marshall puts his hands up, saying, "The parties over!" Later that night, Marshall and Stacey are asleep in the bed, and there is a loud knock at the door that wakes Marshall up. Marshall, sweating, sits up and starts yelling at Stacey, "WHO THE FUCK YOU GOT COMING TO MY DOOR!"

Marshall wakes Stacey up, and she tries to say something, but he slaps the shit out of her, and she cowers in fear. Marshall, still drunk and high, loses it and says, "So you think I'm fuckin around bitch!"

Marshall hears the door starting to knock louder, and Marshall runs downstairs to the garage, and he grabs a gallon of gas. Marshall comes back through the kitchen and grabs a box of matches. Then he runs back upstairs and throws the gas on Stacey, and she yells, "HELP ME! THIS MOTHERFUCKERS CRAZY!"

George at the door, hearing her scream kicks the door in. Then he runs upstairs to see Marshall trying to strike the match, but it won't light. Marshall's hands are wet, covered in gas, but he keeps on striking the match. George runs into the room, tackling Marshall to the floor, and Marshall breaks down crying in his longtime friend's arms.

George, consoling Marshall, says, "Marshall, it will be all right... we gone get you some help, my brother."

Stacey, still scared, timidly comes over to Marshall putting her arms around him, and the two break down crying.

RECORDING STUDIO - EVENING - WINTER 1977

The song "O-H-I-O" by the Ohio Players plays in the studio. Satch is in the studio's control room with two girls on a couch. Satch having one on his lap and the other rubbing his ear sitting next to him. Marshall and Pee Wee walk in, and Satch jumps up, pointing at the control board, saying, "Check this out. This is gonna be our state's anthem. Told y'all putting up our own money was the way to go! More money, baby!"

Satch, being excited, takes a big hit of cocaine, then Marshall and Pee Wee walk out the room. In the lobby are two groupies, getting high, and you see a male groupie half asleep on the chair and the female groupie lighting a spoon on fire with her arm tied with a thick rubber band.

Pee Wee sits down and tries to hand Marshall some coke, but he gestures no. Marshall starts looking at everyone, disgusted. Then Marshall turns to Pee Wee and says, "Look at us! We haven't practiced in three weeks. And we missed two shows this month already. Look around. I don't even know half these motherfuckers! Word around town is we lost our magic and are headed for self-destruction. Pee Wee, I'm glad I went to rehab!"

Marshall looks over to Pee Wee, and you see Pee Wee has already nodded off in the seat. Marshall shakes his head and walks out. At this time, Stach starts a new group on the side "Faze O," spawning their hit "Riding High." Also, in Nineteen-seventy-seven, Actor Fred Willimson asked the Players to do a soundtrack for a film he was working on entitled "Mr. Mean." The Players also got the opening scene to the movie play in a club. Satch also got a line talking to Actor Fred Willimson in the movie.

DOWNTOWN DAYTON - SUMMER 1978 - DAY

Satch and Sugarfoot in Satch's Lotus are driving in Downtown Dayton, Ohio. Sugarfoot is so high he starts swerving, and an officer parked up on the side of the road sees this and pulls them over. Satch high and nervous stuff the coke in-between the seat.

When the officer gets to Satch's car door, he sees powder on Satch's nose. He pulls out his gun from the holster, then points it at Satch, and the officer yells, "HANDS WHERE I CAN SEE EM... DON'T MOVE! GET OUT THE CAR, NOW!"

Satch gets out of the car, and the officer places him on his knees with his hands on his head. The officer looks in the car, and he sees four ounces of coke tucked in the seat. The Officer finding this much coke in Dayton gets nervous, and he points his gun at Sugarfoot's face in the driver's seat and yells, "OUT OF THE CAR NOW! GET ON YOUR KNEES NEXT TO YOUR FRIEND!"

Sugarfoot puts his hands up, then comes around the car and gets on his knees next to Satch, and the officer starts to cuff the two of them.

Satch and Sugarfoot were on their way to Billie's ranch, so with their one call Satch called his wife, but there was no answer. Sugarfoot calls over to Billie's ranch, knowing that everybody should be their especially Pee Wee. At Billie's Ranch are two naked Hippie girls high, running around twirling until they see Pee Wee off to the side playing his trumpet. They chase him and trap him in a barn. Billy laughs, seeing this while walking to the house. Billy opens the door and hears the phone ringing, and he rushes to answer it. "Hello." Sugarfoot in the jail gets relieved as Billie answers, "BILLY, Billy, man, I'm glad I caught you... Me and Satch just got locked up! Tell Pee Wee he always has that little black book with all those numbers. It's not looking good. We got locked up downtown with four ounces. Tell him to call now. Thanks, man."

Billy puts his hand on his head. Then he runs to the barn where he saw Pee Wee is at. Billy, seeing that the stall door is closed, he knocks and says, "They got Satch and Foots!"

Pee Wee, peeking only his hand out, passes a little black book, and in a muffled tone, he says, "Here call the lawyer, his numbers on the first page. I'm high and busy, later!" Pee Wee closes the door, and you hear the ladies giggling.

The song "Contradiction" by the Ohio Players plays (Not even going to say it this time.)

On a cold winter night, hold on! Let me start that again on a cold Dayton, Ohio night Marshall and Stacey are snuggled up in a blanket on the sofa, in front of a burning fireplace. You see them feeding each other strawberries and drinking fine wine. Stacey rolls over and looks Marshall in the face, and in the sweetest, softest tone, she says, "Marshall, through all the bullshit who'd ever had thought that kiss would've last 4 years. I love you." Marshall

being playful, says, "You want to show me."
Marshall kisses Stacey and pulls the cover over
their heads. According to Marshall, this was "the
best time of his life."

NIGHT CLUB - NIGHT - SPRING 1978

The song "Can You Still Love Me" by the Ohio
Players plays, the band performing to a thin crowd.
They look and sound horrible. A man in the
audience comes to the front of the stage looking
angry, and he yells over the music, "MAN, GIVE
IT UP... BOO!!!" No one but a drunk lady keeps
dancing. Just like that, the Players have lost their
Midas touch. Marshall looks at his bandmates,
disgusted, knowing what they have been through all
these years.

REHEARSAL STUDIO IN DAYTON, OHIO -
AFTERNOON

Marshall, waiting at the band's rehearsal for the
band to show up to the studio, but the Studio is
dirty. Marshall looks at the clock, and it is three pm.
After waiting for hours and cleaning the whole
studio, it's dark, and no one has shown up. Marshall
checks the clock, and it's nine pm on the clock.
Then he turns off the lights and walks out, locking

the door leaving his right hand on the door as if it's the last time.

REHAB CENTER DAYTON, OHIO

Marshall is sitting in a black Mercedes Benz, Looking at a magazine in front of a rehab center in Dayton, Ohio. Pee Wee walking out looking really revitalized and refreshed. Pee Wee, noticing Marshall is not paying attention, puts his bag down then sneaks up to Marshall on the passenger side. Pee Wee, in his deepest voice, yells, "GIVE ME YOUR MONEY MOTHERFUCKER!"

Marshall jumps, then smiles, looking at how refreshed Pee Wee looked. Marshall smiling and real happy to see how good Pee Wee looks, says, "Man, anybody coming out here to rob somebody gotta be the stupidest crook in the book! Lookin real good, my brother, let me check you out." Pee Wee puts both arms out, letting Marshall check him out, then he jumps in the car. Then Pee Wee turns to Marshall and says, "First off, before you say something and just mess this up, I just want to thank you for saving my life. That drinking..."

Marshall cuts him off, finishing the sentence saying, "Is a thing of the past. Remember when you met me?" Pee Wee looks at Marshall as he seems serious and says, "Yeah!" Marshall puts the car back in the park. Then he turns to face Pee Wee. Marshall looking Pee Wee in the eyes, says, "When you met me, I was in it for the girls, thinking if I was in a band, I could have any one of them I wanted!

Marshall elbows Pee Wee, and Pee Wee smiles, Marshall having his attention, says, "But after the first year and Robert. I saw that it was more than just a way to get girls or money to get girls! It was bout family! I reluctantly had to give that up to make myself a better person. We became closer than our own families. Pee Wee, me you Foots and Satch, we made it! Look at the cars and houses! Marshall pauses, and Pee Wee nods his head, agreeing. Then Marshall says, "We might not be on top no more, but it was one hell of a love roller-coaster, huh?" Pee Wee shakes his head and smiles; then the car drives off.

DICK CLARK'S ROCKIN NEW YEARS - DECEMBER 31, 1978

The Players are back-stage at Dick Clark Rockin New Year without Satch. Sugarfoot is being interviewed by a reporter off to the side while Billy is going over sound levels with a young white stagehand. Marshall and Pee Wee are sitting at a table, Marshall is tuning his Bass, and Pee Wee is wiping his horn off. Pee Wee, concerned and a little nervous, looks over to Marshall, looking down at his guitar, and he says, "Nobody seen Satch yet? We go on in five."

As he says that, Satch walks in the door with a sexy light-skinned black woman laced in diamonds and gold looking as high as a kite. The door knocks, then opens, and it's Dick Clark's Assistant, a young white female; then she walks in, and with a tiny little voice, she says, "Fellas, it's showtime!"

Satch reaches into his jacket pocket for a gold case. He opens it and takes a hit of cocaine in both nostrils. Then the woman with Satch puts her hand out demanding money with a nasty attitude tapping her foot and pushing her lip up. Satch reaches in his pocket and gives her a wad of cash. Marshall, seeing this, taps Pee Wee and says, "Look at this motherfucker, and we bout to our biggest shows ever!"

Marshall, fixated on Satch, starts shaking his head while looking at Satch and the woman he's with. Then all of a sudden, he smiles at Pee Wee and says, "Wait, is that dirty, Debbie?" Pee Wee puts his hand on his head in amazement, then smiles at Marshall, saying, "She ain't dirty Debbie no more!

Shit, she might as well be in the band; cause she's getting paid."

Sugarfoot looking confused, rushes over to Marshall and Pee Wee and says, "Aye, that's Dirty Debbie?" Marshall and Pee Wee both bust out laughing. Sugarfoot catches on and joins in, then Sugarfoot puts an arm around Marshall and the other around Pee Wee while they walk past Satch fusing with Dirty Debbie. They all look at Satch then shake their heads as they walk out to cameras flashing and groupies backstage.

NEW YORK CITY TIMES SQUARE
DECEMBER 31, 1978

New York City, Times Square December 31st, 1978, all eyes are set on the ball about to drop, all major networks cameras worldwide then look to one of the largest crowds in the world. To see an estimated one million people feeling hope waving signs saying hello mom from New York... Texas, Canada, welcome 1978 to cameras passing by as America and the world get ready.

THE CAMERA PANS TO THE STAGE IN SLOW MOTION as you hear the countdown from the crowd's loud unisence chant, "EIGHT, SEVEN." The camera focuses on Sugarfoot then pans left into each band member's face except Marshall. Pee Wee turns to Marshall smiling, and because of all the noise, he speaks loudly, "Hey Marshall do you have any regrets?" At this point, the CAMERA PANS LEFT: to Marshall holding his bass guitar with his head down, replies, "NOT ONE!!!"

The crowd yells, "One." Marshall picks his head up, and the whole group with Sugarfoot at lead yells, "FIRE!!!!" The band giving one of the hottest stages shows performances, performing "Fire" for one million-plus, rocking Times Square. After their performance Andy Gibbs performed "I Just Want To Be Your Everything." then the "Ohio Players" returned with "Good Luck Stacey," followed by KC & The Sunshine Band performing "Wrap Your Arms Around Me." This line-up needed a deal closer, so the Ohio Players unleashed their most popular record even till today, "Love Rollercoaster," closing the show and becoming Marshall's "highest point in his career."

HOME OF MR. AND MRS. MARSHALL JONES - DAY - SUMMER 79

Stacey, in the kitchen fixing lunch, hears the telephone ringing. Stacey puts down the butter knife and the slice of bread, then wipes her hand on her way to answer the phone. "Hello." Stacey's demeanor changes and she says, "Sure, one moment, please." Stacey, looking concerned, puts the phone on the counter and walks out the back door towards the garage. In the garage, Marshall is working on his Porsche engine.

Stacey walks into the garage sounding and looking worried, and she says, "Honey, there's a phone call for you. It sounds real important." This catches Marshall's attention the way she says it. He turns around with his socket wrench and answers the call on the phone on the wall in the garage. "Hello." The IRS Agent sounding very obnoxious, says, "Mr. Jones?" Marshall replies, "Yes." The IRS Agent, just trying to be annoying, tries to get way up under Marshall's skin, saying, "Mister Marshall Eugene Jones? Marshall replied sternly, "Yes! Now, who's this?" Marshall waiting because of the brief pause, mouths the words, "What the fuck?" Then the IRS Agent being condescending, introduces himself, "Mr. Jones, I'm an investigator with the IRS.

Marshall replies, "The IRS?" Stacey puts her hand on his head while Marshall listens to the IRS Agent's reply, "Yes, Mr. Jones, and we need to talk soon to clear up a few matters." Marshall hears the words come in, and it rattles his cage and, with a slight crack in his voice, says, "What you talking about? My records are impeccable." At this point, Stacey, not knowing what is going on, starts to fan herself. The IRS Agent, with a chuckle in his voice, replies, "Well, Mr. Jones, you might want to bring those records with you tomorrow morning downtown." Marshall hangs the phone up and sees Stacey fanning herself, sitting on a chair by the door.

The next morning Marshall and Stacey show up at the federal building in Downtown Dayton, Ohio. Marshall holding Stacey's hand stops, then he looks up at the building. Stacey squeezes his hand and the two walk in. Marshall and Stacey sit in a tiny little office, and the investigator, a middle-aged white Ohioan. The investigator walks in the room then he sits at his desk to a waiting Marshall and Stacey. Marshall, looking worried, leans forward and says, "You went through the books for an hour. How did it check out?" The IRS agent pats Marshall's books sitting on the desk, then with a wicked grin on his face and a reel condescending tone, he replies, "Mr. Jones, I have to say, yes, your books are, in fact impeccable." Marshall looking confused, says, "Then what's the problem?"

The investigator opens a file containing copies of many checks. He starts handing Marshall numerous unknown checks written by Satch. The Investigator smiling, still grabbing check after check, says, "OK, this check is for a condo in LA. This one is for a new car three weeks ago in LA. A condo in Chicago all signed by Clarence Satchel, need I go on Mr.

189

Jones?" Marshall puts both hands on his head, and the investigator sitting there smiling says, "You are the treasure, right?"

Marshall puts his head down and starts to tap his foot. Stacey, worried by the look on Marshall's face, says, "Marshall, you alright?" Marshall doesn't answer, and Stacey looks over to the investigator and says, "I never seen him like this?" Marshall, without looking at anyone, blurts out, "Satch played me! He played me from the start... Treasurer? Fuck!

Bright early on a Tuesday morning, here I am walking up to this Backstabbing bastard's door, mad as a Motherfucker! Marshall starts banging on the front door of a nice home in Dayton, Ohio. Marshall gets more frustrated as no one comes to the door. He starts to tap his foot and then proceeds to bang the door with more authority, commanding a response! All of a sudden, a matted-looking afro, along with the face of someone that has been to the moon and back three times, opens the door. Marshall is not going for the pathetic look on the thirty-eight-year-old Clarence "Satch" Satchell is trying to give, as he was woken from what looked to be a coffin. Satch tries to say something but is bumped out the way as Marshall barges his way into the house. Satch's demeanor changes as you can see that this did not sit well with him. He closes the door shaking his head. Satch walks up to Marshall, and he says, "Hey man, you all right?"

Marshall walks dead up in Satch, looking him dead in his eye, and says, "ALL RIGHT? I got a call from the IRS and…." Satch interrupts Marshall acting humble and apologetic, then he grabs Marshall's arm and says, "Let me explain, man." Marshall slaps Satch's hand off of his arm, and he starts to look Satch dead in his eyes; then he says, "Ain't nothing to explain! They called me cause I'm the treasurer! Satch, we put our trust in you! What the fuck, Satch! Condos in LA, cars, jewelry, trips? You tricked all our money to impress bitches? Cause the band gonna want to know?"

Satch turns around then reaches for an expensive-looking sterling silver tray sitting on his coffee table with cocaine on it. Satch tries his best to ignore Marshall; he doesn't catch eye contact with him at all. Then Satch puts his hand out, gesturing to wait a minute, then he says, "Hold on, man. Let me get something for my head." Then Satch looks at Marshall with a look that could freeze ice then he says, "Don't tell the group nothin!"

Satch snorts a thick line of cocaine, pauses, then looks at Marshall with a wicked smile on his face and says, "I got an idea, we get back in the studio and create some fire again! what do you say, man?"

Satch tries to touch Marshall's arm again to plead his case, but Marshall looks him at him like he's crazy, and he yells, "YOU THAT FUCKIN STUPID! Satch there investigating us!"

Satch starts to grovel as Marshall turns to walk off, and Satch says, "C'mon man, I'll pay for your house; that way, they can't take it." Marshall turns around enraged, and he says, "It was you, me, Pee Wee, Greg, and Foots that started this! And you broke our brotherhood, snatching all of our dreams! Remember your own words, "One mind!" Satch, we trusted you! It's over, YOU FIRED! Look at you! Do you even know what you've done?"

Marshall walks out and leaves the door open, and you see Satch standing in the doorway, looking high and sick.

THE HOMES OF THE OHIO PLAYERS

The song "Here Today Gone Tomorrow" by the Ohio Players plays. Still selling this ambiance. After firing Satch, the Players once again find themselves in tax problems. One by one, the Players have all their assets seized. First to lose it all is Billy Beck; they took his houses, cars, watches, etc... Billy and his family stand outside as they remove item after item from what used to be one of his greatest accomplishments.

Sugarfoot and Pee Wee both are up next, losing their homes, cars, etc... Followed by the rest of the band members. At this point, the band was burnt; forget about being on fire!!!

Marshall, out on the street with his wife and kids, broke down and cried like a baby as the marshals removed all of Marshall's worldly possessions from what used to be his family's home. This would be the last and final breakup of the Multi-Platinum "Ohio Players."

By nineteen- eighty-two, Satch gets convicted for under-reporting income he earned and went to Jail. Satch's wife Carolyn divorces him for numerous affairs.

Marshall "Rock" Jones said, and I quote, "Just like that, the magic was over! With disco in, we were dinosaurs! All of my partners have passed, and I miss them… to the point that I have served my time here! You know how people talk bout Lebron James being the best basketball player... when it comes to me... I may not be the best, but the best know about me... that is enough for me."

Still setting the ambiance with the "Ohio Players" song "Heaven."

DATES OF DEATHS OF THE BAND MEMBERS

Marshall "Rock" Jones was a good friend. I had the pleasure of living with Marshall for six months to compile this story. Living in the neighborhood where it all started gave me every opportunity to absorb the essence of this story. Marshall died of cancer on May 27, 2016, in Houston, Texas, at the age of 75.

Greg Webster the last man standing, died at the age of 84 on January 14th, 2022. He was the last surviving member of the "Ohio Players" original lineup. Greg had the most children, so I named him Biggest Player. We made many jokes about this during our taping. Greg was very informative and inspiring, and in my opinion the funkiest drummer I've ever heard. G-funk thrived on his drum patterns on track "Funky Worm." Thank you, my brother!

Clarence "Satch" Satchell died of a brain aneurysm at The Good Samaritan Hospital on Saturday, December 30, 1995, in Dayton, Ohio. Satch was 55 years old. Satch died with his wife Rafat Nasrin Satchell, his five daughters, and longtime friend and bandmate Marshall "Rock" Jones by his side. Having the pleasure of meeting Rafat Nasrin

Satchell during Marshall's Interview to hear that Marshall gave Satch Jr. his first haircut, let us just say friendship was more powerful than money.

The "Ohio Players'" Frontman Leroy "Sugarfoot" Bonner, known for his double-neck guitar and unique vocals, died on January 26, 2013, of cancer.

The Ohio Players Trumpeter Ralph "Pee Wee" Middlebrook, Pee Wee died of cancer on December 30, 1997. Rest in Paradise!

The "Ohio Untouchables" founder, frontman, and amazing guitarist Robert Ward died December 25, 2008.

Cornelius "Cornbread" Johnson died on February 1, 2009.

Junie Morrison died on January 21, 2017.

Shaun Dedrick died on May 2, 2018, following an illness. I had the pleasure of meeting Shaun at his house and also getting his father-in-law George Robuck to help me with getting this story together.

SPECIAL THANKS TO:

Marshall "Rock" Jones and Greg Webster for the amazing interviews and stories we used to compile the story.

THE END

Made in the USA
Monee, IL
05 October 2022

15290412R00108